JOHN COX

First published in Great Britain in 1993
by Philip's, a division of Octopus Publishing Group Ltd,
2–4 Heron Quays, London E14 4JP

Second edition 1996
Reprinted with revisions 1997
Third edition 1999

This new revised and expanded edition published 2005



Horizon 35°S by courtesy of Fergus Veitch.

The Author would like to thank Frances Button for her help in preparing this new edition.

The etymologies on p.12 are taken from Paul Kunitzsch and Tim Smart, *Short Guide to Modern Star Names and their Derivations*, Harrassowitz, Wiesbaden (1986).

ISBN-13 978-0-540-08792-1
ISBN-10 0-540-08792-0



Printed in China

Details of other Philip's titles and services can be found on our website at: **www.philips-maps.co.uk**

*Title page: M6 in Scorpius, an open cluster of predominantly blue stars, is one of a number of naked-eye visible open clusters in this region of sky.*

Picture credits

***Title page***: *N.A.Sharp, Mark Hanna, REU program/NOAO/AURA/NSF*
***13*** *Rob Gendler*
***19*** *Robin Scagell/Galaxy*
***20*** *NASA/JPL/USGS*
***24*** *Jay Ouellet*
***58, 60*** *Robin Scagell/Galaxy*
***61*** *John Cox*
***62t*** *Robin Scagell/Galaxy*
***62b*** *John Cox*
***63*** *Stephen Pitt*
*Milky Way pp.14–15 © John Cox*
*Star maps © John Cox & Richard Monkhouse*
*Artworks © Philip's*

# CONTENTS

# Introduction

The *Philip's Pocket Star Atlas* is designed to help a new observer to identify the stars, planets and constellations, and to serve as a minimum atlas for the traveller and the more experienced observer.

The best conditions for observing the stars and planets are dark, clear skies, when the stars appear brighter and more stars can be seen. A bright Moon washes out the fainter stars. The street lighting used in towns and cities creates difficulties for the urban observer, but the planets and the brighter stars of the major constellations can be seen in the middle of a city provided the observer chooses a clear and otherwise dark night and avoids having nearby lights shining into the eyes: in other words, if he or she observes from somewhere in local shadow. Low-cost telescopes advertised as 'suitable for astronomy' are often of little practical use, and are frequently a source of disappointment. Low-magnification binoculars (7× or 8×) are by far the most useful kind of telescope for the beginner, and have many specialized uses for the more experienced observer.

# The celestial sphere

All the objects of the night sky – the stars, the planets and the Moon – are at enormous and varying distances, with the more distant objects thousands of millions of times more distant than the nearer, but to the human eye they all seem to be equally far away, as if placed on the inside of a gigantic 'celestial sphere' that encloses the Earth in the way that a shell encloses an egg. Although the celestial sphere is an illusion, it is a useful convention, and it is used to describe where celestial objects appear to be.

Over the course of the night the stars appear to rise in the east and set in the west. This is an apparent motion produced by the rotation of the Earth; a more familiar manifestation is the apparent motion of the Sun over the course of the day. At night the Earth's rotation makes it look as if the whole sky is moving as a piece, as if the imaginary celestial sphere is rotating round the Earth.

## Celestial coordinates

The position of a celestial object is given by a system of celestial coordinates that work like terrestrial latitude and longitude projected on to the inside of the (imaginary) celestial sphere. The points overhead of the terrestrial poles are called the north and south celestial poles. The circle of sky that passes overhead when observed from the terrestrial equator is called the celestial equator.

The angular distance of an object north or south from the celestial equator is reckoned in degrees of declination. Declination is related to

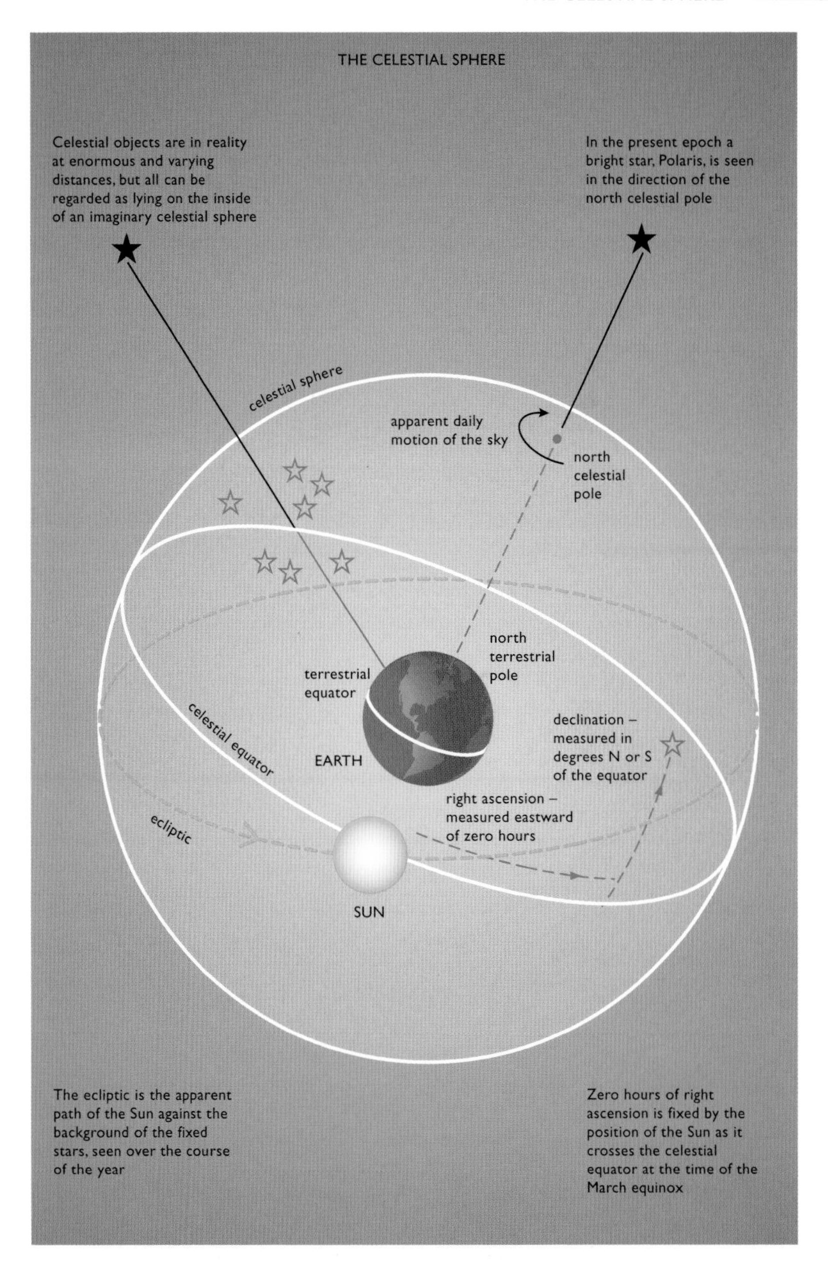


▲ *In this diagram the celestial sphere is seen from the outside, looking in, but on the star maps it is seen from the inside, looking out.*

terrestrial latitude; objects at a given declination north or south will pass overhead of an observer on the same terrestrial latitude.

The angular distance of an object round the sphere is usually measured in hours and minutes of right ascension (RA). Right ascension is reckoned in degrees eastward of the position of the Sun as it crosses the celestial equator at the time of the equinox in March: the vernal equinox for the northern hemisphere of the Earth. This position is called the First Point of Aries. There are 24 hours of RA altogether, so each hour of RA is equivalent to 15° of arc.

## *The fixed stars*

The Earth is a member of the Solar System, one of nine planets (not counting the minor planets and asteroids) in orbit round a central star, the Sun. The Earth orbits the Sun at an average distance of 150 million km (93 million miles). Light, travelling at approximately 300,000 km per second (186,000 miles per second), takes eight minutes to travel from the Sun to the Earth. The nearest naked-eye star beyond the Sun is Alpha Centauri, lying at a distance of 4.3 light-years, which is to say that light takes 4.3 years to travel from it to us. Most of the stars visible to the naked eye (meaning visible without telescopes or optical aids) are very much farther away.

When the positions of stars are carefully measured through telescopes over a period of years it can be worked out that they are moving about in independent directions at high speeds. However, their distances from us and each other are so great that these movements do not show to the naked eye, and the stars appear 'fixed' in the same positions relative to one another. Changes will eventually become apparent, but over a few thousand years the relative position of the stars looks the same.

## *The ecliptic*

The Earth takes 365¼ days to orbit the Sun. From the viewpoint of the Earth it looks as if the Sun is moving along a path traced out against the background of the fixed stars – or would look like that if the stars could be seen while the Sun was in the sky. In practice the position of the Sun against the stars can be directly observed only during a total solar eclipse, when the brighter stars become visible. The apparent path of the Sun is called the ecliptic, taking its name from being the path on which eclipses of the Sun and Moon are seen to take place.

The Moon and the planets all appear to circle the sky within a few degrees of the ecliptic, and their positions along it can be measured in degrees of celestial longitude eastwards from the First Point of Aries (longitude 0°). The Sun appears to move 1° eastward along the ecliptic

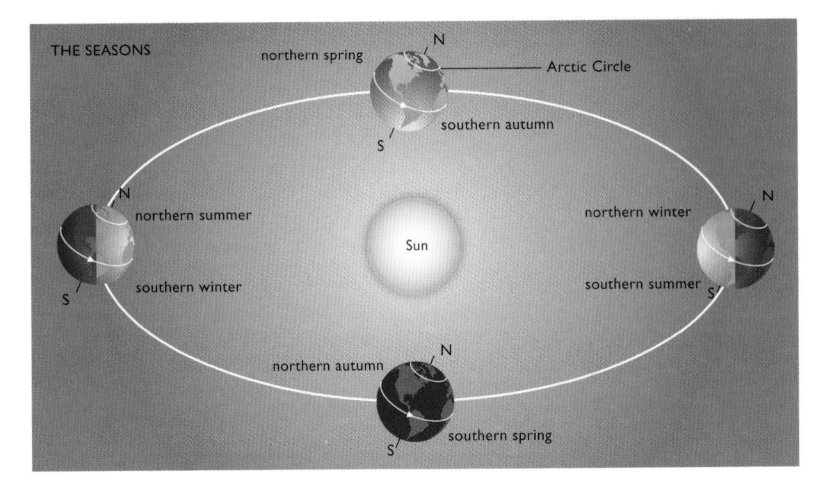


▲ *Winter and Summer in the temperate regions of the Earth are produced by the tilt of the axial plane of the spinning Earth relative to the plane of the Earth's orbit round the Sun (the plane of the ecliptic).*

in 24 hours, an effect of the Earth's westward motion in its orbit round the Sun.

The axis of the Earth's spin is not square to the plane of the Earth's orbit round the Sun – the plane of the ecliptic – but is tilted over at an angle of 23.45°. The plane of the Earth's axial rotation is taken as primary, so the angle between the plane of rotation and the plane of the orbit is known as the inclination of the ecliptic. It figures in a number of effects, including the seasons of winter and summer in the temperate regions of the Earth. For half of the year one hemisphere is tilted towards the Sun, making the long days and short nights of summer; for the other half of the year the same hemisphere is tilted away, making the short days and long nights of winter.

In summer in the temperate regions of the northern hemisphere the Sun rises above the horizon in a direction (azimuth) north of east, passes high through the sky, and sets in a direction north of west. In winter the Sun rises south of east, passes low through the sky, and sets south of west. In the southern hemisphere the pattern is reversed, with the Sun rising north of east in winter, and south of east in summer. The most northerly and most southerly rising and setting positions, and the longest and shortest days, are reached at the times of the solstices (around 21 June and 21 December). See the diagrams on page 8.

At the time of the equinoxes (around 20 March and 23 September) the Sun passes directly overhead of the observer at the terrestrial equator. Observed from anywhere on the inhabited earth it appears to rise due east and set due west, and the lengths of day and night are exactly 12 hours each (hence the name *equinox*, 'equal night').

## *Meridian passage*

A meridian is any great circle that passes through both of the poles. The phrase 'observer's celestial meridian' describes an imaginary line that starts from the horizon at due north, passes directly over the observer, and meets the horizon at due south. The Sun crosses this meridian at true local midday (from the Latin *meridies*, 'midday'). When a celestial object crosses the meridian it is said to be at meridian passage. Other terms that describe the same event are culmination and upper transit.

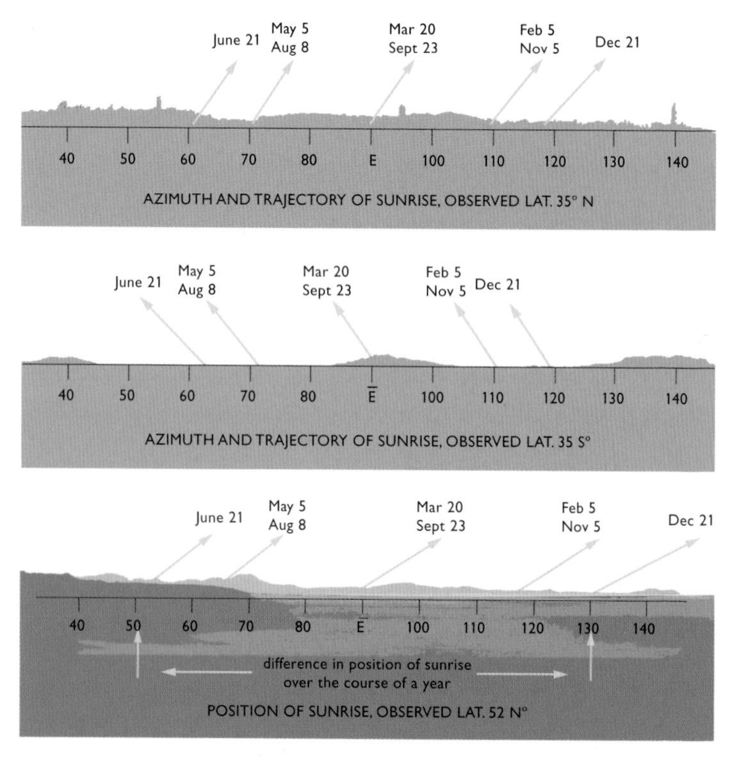


▲ *Rising points of the Sun. The direction, called the 'azimuth', of sunrise and sunset depends on the latitude of observation. The overall range of azimuth is greater at higher latitudes than at lower. From the temperate regions of the northern hemisphere the daytime Sun passes through South. From the temperate regions of the southern hemisphere the daytime Sun passes through north.*

► *Looking north from the northern hemisphere the celestial pole coincides with the position of the bright star Polaris. Over the course of the night the circumpolar stars are seen rotating in an anticlockwise direction. Looking south from the southern hemisphere there is no bright star in the direction of the south celestial pole. The celestial pole lies between the bright stars shown on the diagram; the stars are seen to rotate in a clockwise direction.*

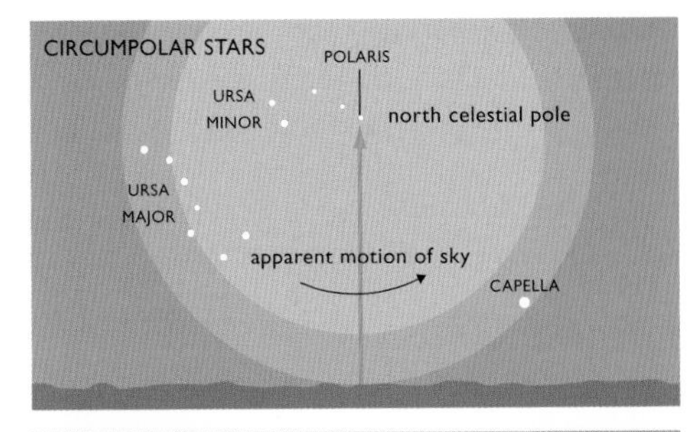


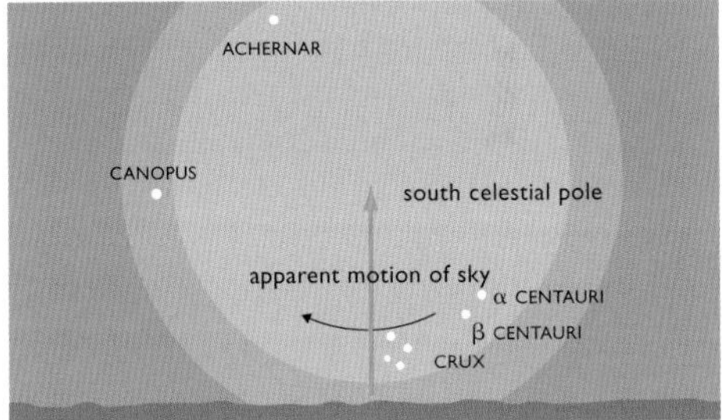


## *Circumpolar stars*

Except for those living close to the terrestrial equator, observers will have a view of either the north or the south celestial polar regions. Stars close to the poles appear to move round in a circle over 24 hours (sidereal hours, see below) and never rise or set. These are called circumpolar stars. A star crossing the meridian above the pole is said to be at upper transit, the same star crossing the meridian below the pole (12 hours later) is said to be at lower transit.

## *Time*

Mean (average) time, or ordinary clock time, is based on the average length of a day and a night. It takes 24 hours on average to get from one midday – one meridian passage of the Sun – to the next. In the same period the Earth travels nearly 1° in its orbit round the Sun; in apparent motion the Sun moves 1° eastward along the ecliptic, so that, in order to bring the Sun back to meridian passage the Earth has to rotate through 361°.

'Sidereal time' is defined by the period that is required to bring the same star from one meridian passage to the next. To bring this about the Earth has only to rotate through 360°. This defines 24 hours of sidereal time ('star time', from the Latin *sideralis*, 'of a star'). Twenty-four hours of sidereal time take up 23 hours and 56 minutes of average mean time. Measured by the clock, the same star returns to meridian passage four minutes earlier every night.

From one night to the next the same stars appear higher in the eastern sky, reach meridian passage sooner, and set sooner. The observer looking out on the sky at the same time every night will notice that over the course of the year the area of sky that is open to view moves slowly eastward over the course of the year. The maps on pages 31–48 show the changing areas of sky that cross the meridian at midnight each month.

### *Sundial time*

The Earth does not orbit the Sun in a perfect circle but in an ellipse with the Sun at one focus. In accordance with Kepler's second law the Earth travels faster when closer to the Sun (and sweeps out equal areas in equal times). The result is that the Sun's apparent motion against the fixed stars is greater at one end of the year (around 3 January), when the Earth is at its closest to the Sun, and lesser at the other (around 3 July).

'Sundial time' takes midday to be when the Sun crosses the meridian. The Earth's spin rate on its axis remains the same, so it takes more than 24 mean (average) hours to bring the Sun back to meridian passage every day in the months around January, and less than 24 hours in the

THE EQUATION OF TIME

The table shows, to an accuracy of about one minute, the time in GMT when the Sun crosses the meridian, observed from longitude 0°, at 5-day intervals. Account should be made for civil time and longitude E or W of Greenwich.

| | | | |
|---|---|---|---|
| Dec 21 1158h | Mar 21 1207h | Jun 24 1202h | Sep 22 1153h |
| Dec 26 1201h | Mar 26 1206h | Jun 29 1203h | Sep 27 1151h |
| Dec 31 1203h | Mar 31 1204h | | |
| | | Jly 04 1204h | Oct 02 1149h |
| Jan 05 1205h | Apr 05 1203h | Jly 09 1205h | Oct 07 1148h |
| Jan 10 1208h | Apr 10 1201h | Jly 14 1206h | Oct 12 1147h |
| Jan 15 1209h | Apr 15 1200h | Jly 19 1206h | Oct 17 1145h |
| Jan 20 1211h | Apr 20 1159h | Jly 24 1207h | Oct 22 1144h |
| Jan 25 1212h | Apr 25 1158h | Jly 29 1206h | Oct 27 1144h |
| Jan 30 1213h | Apr 30 1157h | | |
| | | Aug 03 1206h | Nov 01 1144h |
| Feb 04 1214h | May 05 1157h | Aug 08 1206h | Nov 06 1144h |
| Feb 09 1214h | May 10 1156h | Aug 13 1205h | Nov 11 1144h |
| Feb 14 1214h | May 15 1156h | Aug 18 1204h | Nov 16 1145h |
| Feb 19 1214h | May 20 1157h | Aug 23 1203h | Nov 21 1146h |
| Feb 24 1213h | May 25 1157h | Aug 28 1201h | Nov 26 1147h |
| | May 30 1158h | | |
| Mar 01 1212h | | Sep 02 1200h | Dec 01 1149h |
| Mar 06 1211h | Jun 04 1158h | Sep 07 1158h | Dec 06 1151h |
| Mar 11 1210h | Jun 09 1159h | Sep 12 1156h | Dec 11 1153h |
| Mar 16 1209h | Jun 14 1200h | Sep 17 1155h | Dec 16 1156h |
| Mar 21 1207h | Jun 19 1201h | Sep 22 1153h | Dec 21 1158h |

months around July. At its maximum rate of change the gain or loss from 24 hours rises to half a minute a day, and the differences add up to maxima in early February when the Sun is 14 mean time minutes 'late' crossing the meridian, and in early November, when it is 16 minutes 'early'.

Meridian passage is in turn specific to the terrestrial longitude of observation. The equation of time relates mean time to sundial time, and this is conveniently done for a given longitude, that is, GMT to sundial time at longitude 0°, as in the table. Further differences are determined by actual longitude of observation, where each degree of longitude west adds a further four minutes of time.

## *The constellations*

From the earliest times observers have in their imagination joined up apparent groupings of stars into the outlines of giant figures, the constellations. In reality most of these figures include stars at enormously different distances, with no true association in three-dimensional space. The major constellations of the northern and equatorial sky are a combination of Mesopotamian and Greek figures, listed by the Greek astronomer Hipparchus in about 130 BC, and transmitted in the *Almagest* (*c.* AD 138) by the Egyptian astronomer and geographer Ptolemy.

Two thousand years ago the ecliptic was divided into 12 sectors, each 30° wide, and named after the constellation found in it. The Sun entered the First Point of Aries (the beginning of the sector containing Aries) at the time of the vernal equinox. One effect of the Moon's gravity is to make the axis of the spinning Earth gyrate slowly, completing one gyration in about 25,760 years. The gyration produces little change in the plane of the ecliptic, but it creates a significant change in the Earth's orientation towards the stars, changing the plane of the celestial equator, and causing the First Point of Aries to move slowly westwards along the ecliptic. Because of this precession, each sector of the ecliptic is now almost 30° removed from the position recorded by Ptolemy.

Minor and southern constellations were added by Europeans in the 16th, 17th and 18th centuries. Constellation boundaries were formalized in 1930. Constellation figures were shown by simplified ball-and-link 'asterisms' in China *c.* 200 BC or earlier.

A table of the constellation names in current scientific use is found on pages 28–30.

## *Star names and designation systems*

A few star names, including Antares, Arcturus, Capella, Sirius, Spica, Regulus, Vindemiatrix, and the star clusters Praesepe and the Pleiades come down from classical antiquity. A number have been introduced in the modern period (Polaris, Atria). Most star names are proper and positional names from Arabic language catalogues adopted and romanized from the 10th century AD onwards and changed in transmission and use (Aldebaran from *al-dabarān*, 'the follower', Achernar from *ākhir al-nahr*, 'the river's end'); many are found in variant and confused forms.

The brighter stars in each constellation were assigned a Greek letter by Johann Bayer in the 17th century, and assigned a number by John Flamsteed in the 18th.

An extension to the Bayer system assigned lower-case letters, a to x, and capital letters, A to Q, to some stars (mostly found in the southern sky). In the 19th century Friedrich Argelander listed variable stars in particular constellations by capital letters from R onwards, in a system that was later extended to double letters and combinations of letters and numbers.

Apart from the stars, which appear pointlike in even the most powerful telescopes, there are a number of more indistinct objects, originally called nebulae. Many of the brighter nebulae were listed by Charles Messier in the 18th century, and are still known by their 'Messier numbers', M1 to M109. A subsequent and more extensive listing was made in Dreyer's *New General Catalogue* of 1888, from which 'NGC numbers' are drawn.

## The Milky Way

The Milky Way is observed as a band of light that crosses the sky, and may be seen over the course of any dark and clear night. Observed through a telescope, the Milky Way is resolved into a swathe of faint stars. Dark patches in the Milky Way are regions of obscuring gas and dust.

The Milky Way is a galaxy system of 200 to 400 thousand million stars, together with vast amounts of gas and dust, arranged in a disc-like shape about 120,000 light-years in diameter. The Sun lies in the plane of the disc about 30,000 light-years from the centre, and the Milky Way is the disc seen edge on. The plane of the Milky Way is represented on maps as the galactic equator. The centre of the Galaxy (0° of galactic longitude) lies beyond the stars that make up Sagittarius. The nearside outer edge (at 180° of galactic longitude) lies beyond the stars of Auriga. The North and South Galactic Poles (NGP and SGP) are located at 90° to the galactic plane.

The Milky Way is one of an estimated 100 thousand million galaxies in the visible universe. Only four external galaxies (galaxies other than our own) are visible to the naked eye. The Large and Small Magellanic Clouds are dwarf irregular galaxies (that is, having no definite shape) at distances of about 160,000 and 200,000 light-years, visible as cloud-like objects in the southern sky. The Andromeda (M31) and Triangulum (M33) galaxies are visible as smudgy objects in the northern sky; both are spiral galaxies similar to our own Milky Way Galaxy, but lying at a distance of more than 2 million light-years.

## Galaxies, star clusters and nebulae

The term 'non-stellar object' has been used to describe any celestial object that does not have the pointlike appearance of a star: galaxies, star clusters and gas clouds. Most of the non-stellar objects shown on the maps are rather dimmer than the faintest stars that are shown, but several are visible with the naked eye under favourable conditions, and most make interesting objects for observation through a pair of binoculars.

External galaxies have been described above. Other kinds of object lie within the Milky Way Galaxy itself. The term 'nebulae' is used to describe vast clouds of dust and gas (mainly hydrogen), often associated with areas in which stars are still being formed. Open clusters are groups of young stars that are presumed to have formed together in the same gas cloud and have not yet drifted apart. Such formations lie along the arms of the Milky Way. Globular clusters are densely populated, compact spherical groups of old stars; they surround the galactic centre in a roughly spherical distribution.

► *Under perfect conditions the spiral galaxy M33 in Triangulum is visible to the naked eye as a faint smudge. Detail is seen in a telescope photograph. The galaxy is about 50,000 ly in diameter, half the diameter of the Milky Way. Red-coloured nebulae are star-forming regions, similar to Milky Way objects the Lagoon Nebula M8 (Equatorial Map 3) and the Orion Nebula M42 (Map 9).*

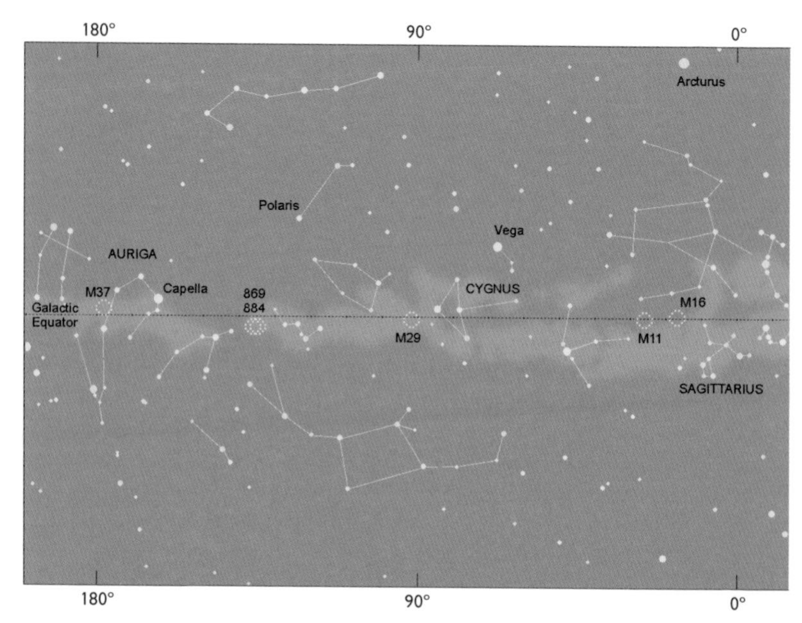
180°
90°
0°
Arcturus
Polaris
Vega
AURIGA
M37
Capella
869
884
CYGNUS
M16
Galactic
Equator
M29
M11
SAGITTARIUS
180°
90°
0°

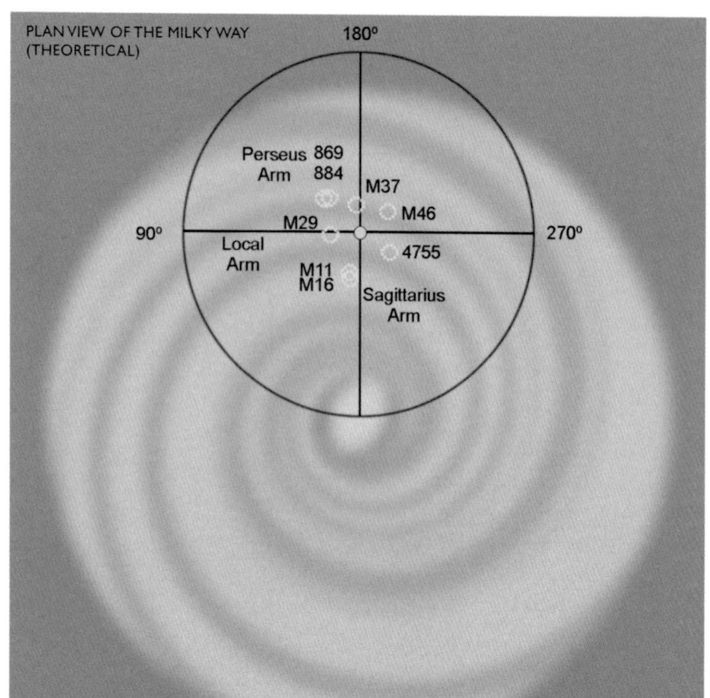
PLAN VIEW OF THE MILKY WAY
(THEORETICAL)
180°
Perseus
Arm
869
884
M37
M46
90°
M29
270°
Local
Arm
4755
M11
M16
Sagittarius
Arm

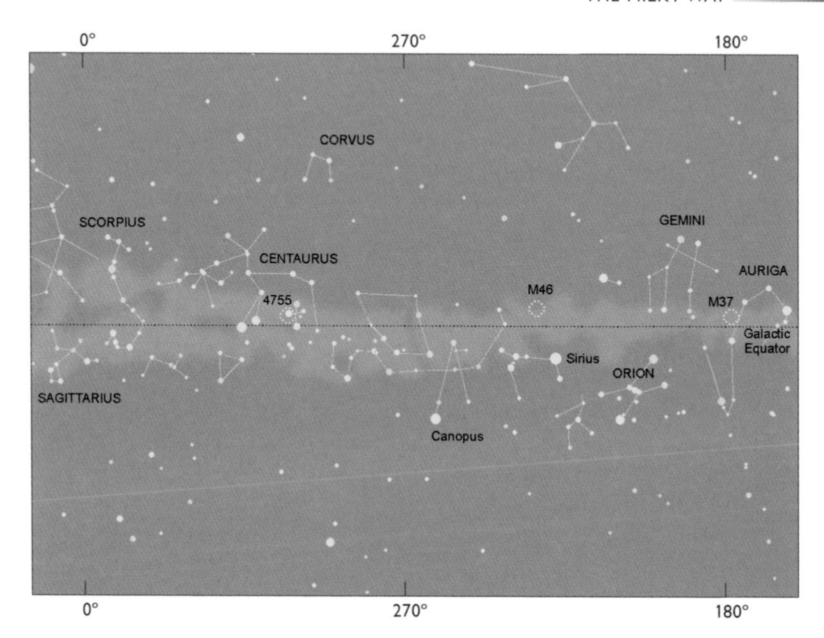


*▲ The Milky Way (above) is a band of light that defines the Milky Way Galaxy, a spiral galaxy of diameter about 100,000 ly, seen edge on. ▼ The Sun lies in the plane of the galaxy about 30,000 ly from the centre (below). The centre of the galaxy lies in the direction of Sagittarius (and beyond the stars composing that constellation); the edge of the galaxy lies in the direction of Auriga. ◀ In plan (left) the Sun, marked by a yellow dot, lies between two spiral arms, here defined by open clusters in Sagittarius, and open clusters in the region of Auriga and Perseus (after which the Perseus Arm is named).*

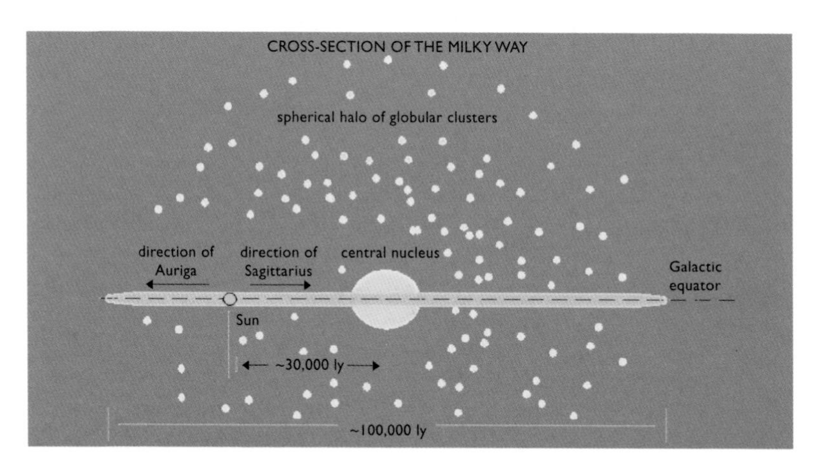

## *Magnitude*

The brightness of stars (and of all celestial objects) is measured in a system of magnitudes, a system inherited from the Greeks, who believed that some stars appeared brighter than others because of their size. It is now clear that the intrinsic brightness of stars varies a great deal, and that another important factor affecting the apparent brightness of a star is its distance. 'Magnitude' is the term still used to describe brightness, but it is used in two ways. Apparent visual magnitude ($m_V$) describes how bright a star appears in the night sky. Absolute visual magnitude ($M_V$) describes how bright a star would appear from a standard distance (≈32.26 light-years), and may be used as a measure of how bright the star is in itself.

In the Greek scale the brightest objects were stars 'of the first magnitude'; less bright stars were stars 'of the second magnitude', down to the dimmest stars that could be seen, stars 'of the sixth magnitude'. The modern scale is much in agreement with the original, but it has been extended through zero and into negative figures in order to accommodate the brightest objects. In addition, it has been recalibrated to make a difference of one magnitude represent a difference of just over 2.5 times the brightness (allowing a difference of five magnitudes to exactly equal a difference of 100 times the brightness). Spica, in Virgo, has an apparent magnitude of +1. Vega, in Lyra, is 2.5 times brighter at $m_V$ 0.0. Sirius, in Canis Major, the brightest star in the sky, has an apparent magnitude of −1.46, 9.6 times as bright as Spica.

Under optimum conditions the faintest stars that can be seen with the naked eye have a $m_V$ of about +6.5. There are about 9000 objects within this limit (shown in a standard reference, *Norton's Star Atlas,* Pearson Education, UK; Pi Press, USA). Apart from a few fainter stars shown for location purposes, the *Philip's Pocket Star Atlas* is limited to $m_V$ 5.1, enough to identify the constellations and to locate the brighter binocular objects.

## *Spectral types*

When the light from a star is passed through a prism (or across a diffraction grating) and focused, its spectrum shows absorption lines that correspond to ionized elements in the atmosphere of the star. Analysis of their spectra allows most stars to be placed on what is in effect a temperature sequence that runs from the hottest '0-type' stars through to the coolest 'M-type' stars. The complete sequence is 0, B, A, F, G, K, M. Each type has subgroups, so that F runs into G through the subgroups F8, F9, G0, G1, G2, G3.... The Sun is of spectral type G2.

When the absolute magnitudes of stars are plotted against their spectral types in (what is known as) the Hertzsprung–Russell

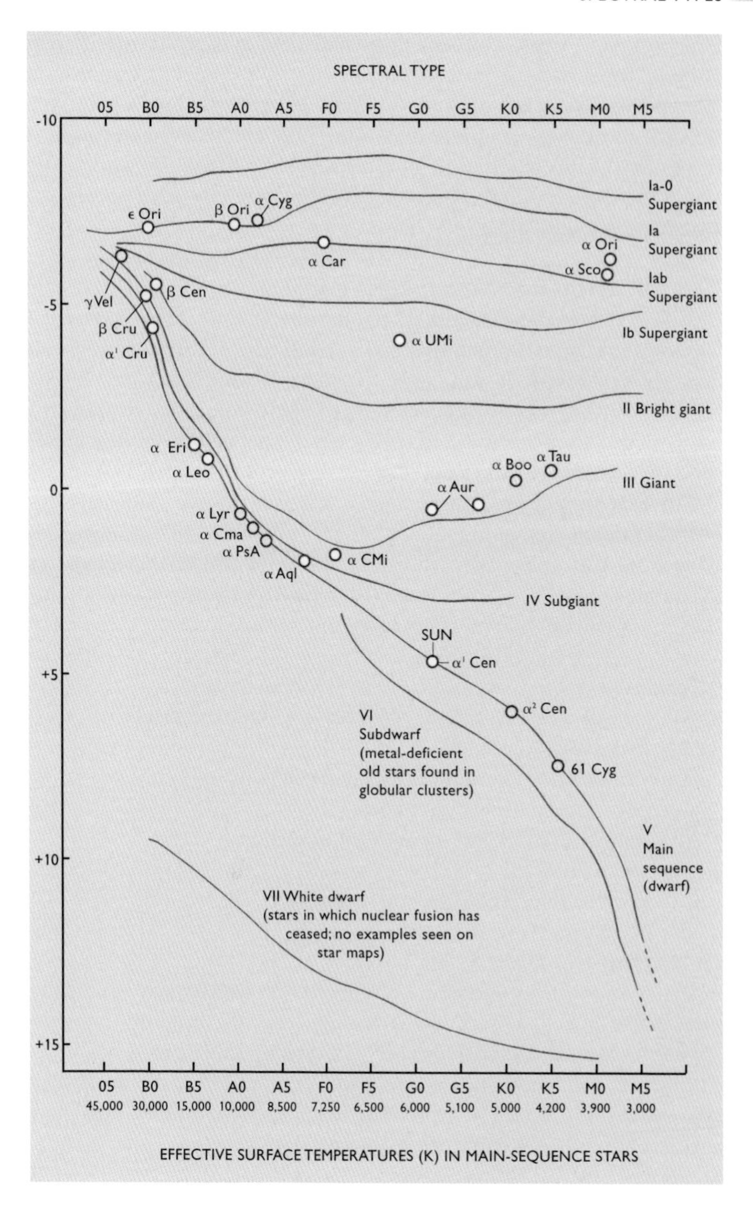


▲ *The Hertzsprung–Russell Diagram shows spectral type (horizontal axis) against absolute magnitude (vertical axis). Most stars are discovered on discrete bands that distinguish compact dwarf stars, such as the Sun and α Centauri (both G2V), from giant and supergiant stars, such as α Tauri and β Orionis.*

Diagram, it is seen that examples fall into a number of discrete groups. Most line up in a 'main sequence' of compact dwarf stars (luminosity class V). A number of stars of exceptional intrinsic brightness are found higher up the diagram. These are believed to be high-mass stars with complicated nuclear reactions that have caused the star to become enormously distended. They are classified as various kinds of giant and supergiant stars.

### *The MK system of classifying stars*

The MK system uses a capital letter and Arabic numeral to describe a star's spectral type, Roman numeral I to VII to describe its luminosity class (note subtypes Ia-0, Ia, Iab, Ib) and following lower-case letters to describe any spectral particularities. The relationship of different luminosity classes is shown against spectral type and absolute magnitude ($M_V$) in the Hertzsprung–Russell diagram (see page 17).

The MK system provides a concise summary of the characteristics of a star, and is used in the table of bright stars (page 49) and the table of variable stars (page 50). Unusual spectral types that are referred to in the tables are WR (Wolf–Rayet, extremely hot stars whose spectra show many emission lines), and S (spectra marked by zirconium lines).

Peculiarity codes used in the tables are these:

e: emission lines – added radiation at specific wavelengths
m: metal absorption lines
n: diffuse lines – produced by rapid rotation
p: pec – peculiarity in spectrum
eq: emission with short wavelength absorption
s: sharp lines
v: variable lines

### *Colours of the stars*

The human eye is not sensitive to colour in very dim objects (hence the black-and-white quality of vision at night) but the brightest stars do appear coloured to the sensitive observer. Red giants such as Betelgeuse, Aldebaran and Antares are distinctly orange-red in appearance, while hot B and A types like Regulus, Sirius, Spica and Vega appear blue to blue-green.

### *Multiple stars*

A double star is any star that can be resolved into two or more elements. There are two types. A 'binary' or 'multiple' star system is a gravitationally bound system involving two or more stars in mutual orbit. An 'optical pair' comprises two independent stars seen along a

► *Compare the red colour of Mars (upper right) with the red colour of the star Antares in Scorpius (lower left). Ares was the Greek counterpart to the Roman god Mars; the name means 'Like to Ares'. Antares is one of a number of bright stars whose colour is apparent to the naked eye.*

chance line-of-sight. A 'naked-eye pair' or 'naked-eye double' can be split – that is, seen to be two stars – by an observer with good eyesight; a 'binocular pair' can be split with binoculars, and a 'telescope pair' with a telescope. The double nature of a 'spectroscopic pair' cannot be observed directly, but instead deduced from analysis of the joint spectrum. Splitting double stars is a favourite test of equipment and can produce interesting, not to say beautiful, contrasts of colour. A list of naked eye and binocular doubles is found in the table on page 51.

### *Variable stars*

The term 'variable star' is applied to stars that show marked variations in brightness. 'Eclipsing binaries', of which the prototype is Algol (β Per), are stable pairs in orbits that bring one star in front of the other in line-of-sight, thus reducing their combined apparent magnitude in a regular eclipse pattern. In contrast, true variables show changes of intrinsic brightness.

Common characteristics of period (regular, semi-regular, unpredictable), luminosity range and spectral type allow variable stars to be grouped after conspicuous prototypes, of which the long-period Mira-type variables are a famous example. A list of variable stars appears on page 51, and includes a number of examples of stars that are visible to the naked eye at maximum but invisible at minimum.

## The Moon

It takes an average of 27.32 days for the Moon to complete (what may conveniently be regarded as) an orbit around the Earth measured in relation to the stars – its sidereal period. This period is not the same as the time from new moon to new moon. The phases of the Moon depend on the relative positions of the Sun, Moon and Earth, and it takes 29.53 days for the same geometry to return; this is known as the synodic period (from the Greek *synodos*, 'coming together').

The Moon's rotation on its own axis is captured by the period of its orbit round the Earth, so that it rotates once in each orbit and always presents the same face to the Earth. Astronomical new moon is the name given to the Moon at conjunction, when it lies in the same direction as the Sun. At astronomical new moon the side of the Moon that faces the Earth is in shadow and cannot be seen.

The Moon is first seen (as what is ordinarily called the new moon) on the second evening after conjunction, when it appears low in the western sky after sunset. Observed from one evening to the next the Moon moves 13° eastward against the stars, appearing higher in the sky each evening and setting 50 minutes later. From one evening to the next it 'waxes', as an increasing proportion of its face is seen illuminated.

Seven to eight days after conjunction the Moon is seen at first quarter; the name may refer to the quarter-sphere that is seen or the quarter-circle angle (90°) that it makes with the Sun. At first quarter the Moon is at the meridian at sunset and sets at midnight.

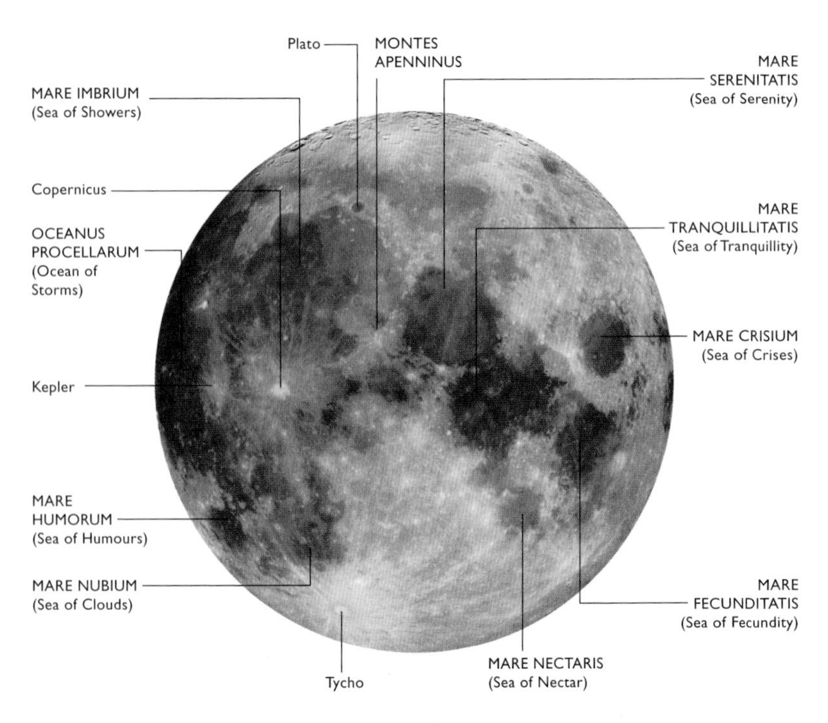


▲ *The principal features of the Moon visible to the naked eye or in a pair of binoculars. The visibility of individual features changes with the phase of the Moon and the angle at which illuminating sunlight strikes the surface.*

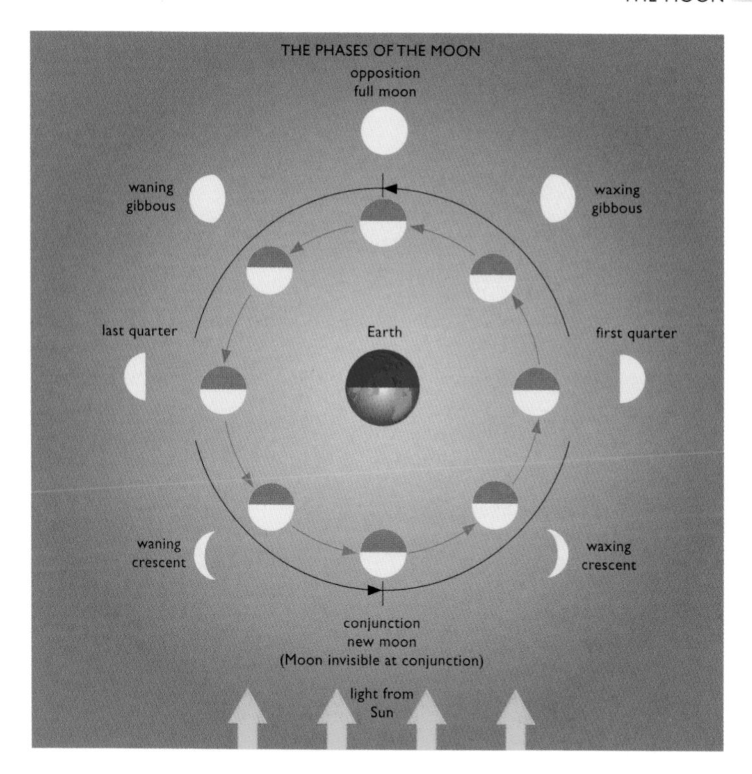


▲ *The phases of the Moon are created by the relative geometry of Sun, Moon and Earth. Except during a lunar eclipse one face of the Moon is always illuminated, but how much can be seen changes as the Moon orbits the Earth.*

Between first quarter and full moon, the Moon appears gibbous (from the Latin for 'humped'). It appears in the eastern sky at sunset, and sets before dawn. Fifteen days after conjunction the whole visible face is illuminated – the full moon. The full moon is 'in opposition' to the Sun; it lies at an angular distance of 180°, rises at sunset, passes the meridian at midnight, and sets at dawn.

After full moon the Moon begins to wane. At last quarter it rises at midnight and reaches the meridian at dawn. The last visible Moon of the cycle is seen usually two days before conjunction, rising before sunrise.

## *Movements of the Sun and Moon compared*

The Moon shows the same patterns of rising and setting seen in the Sun, and the same patterns of passing high or low across the sky, but while the Sun takes a year to exhibit the whole pattern, the Moon

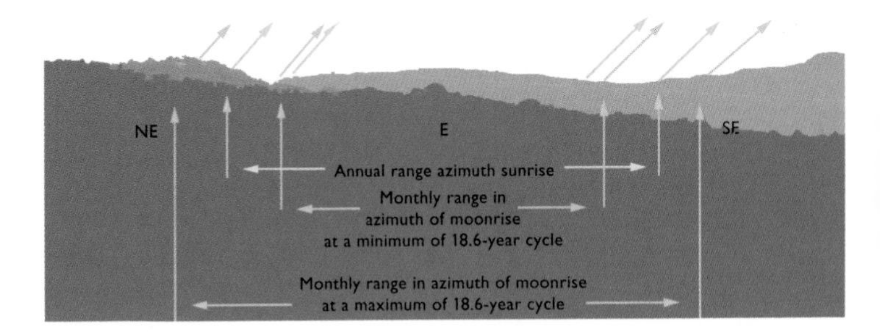


▲ *The diagram shows the range of the change in the rising point (azimuth) of the Moon observed over the course of the month at its minimum at one end of the 18.6-year cycle, and at its maximum at the other end of the 18.6-year cycle.*

shows the full range of movements in the course of a tropical month of 27.3 days (from the Greek *tropikós*, 'turning').

The Moon's orbit round the Earth is inclined to the plane of the ecliptic at an angle of 5.15°, and the points of intersection (the nodes) circle the ecliptic westwards in 18.6 years. For nine years the inclination of the Moon's orbit is additive to that of the ecliptic, so that the monthly extremes of the Moon's position are greater than the yearly extremes of the Sun. For the other nine years inclination is subtractive, so that the Moon's extreme positions are less than the yearly extremes of the Sun. The Moon reaches a maximum range in May 2006, a minimum in September 2015, another maximum in 2025.

## Tides

Subject to the equation of time (see pages 10–11) the Sun makes meridian passage (that is, upper transit) at noon, and lower transit at midnight (see page 8). The Moon describes an orbit of the Earth every 27.32 days. Every day it moves 13° east against the fixed stars, 12° east relative to the Sun. On average the Moon arrives at meridian passage 48 minutes later each day. It takes the Moon an average of 12h 24m to get from upper transit to lower transit, and this is the average time interval from one sea tide to the next.

In a simplified model, the sea on the side of the Earth nearest to the Moon is drawn up by gravity attraction, producing a bulge. On the far side of the Earth, where the Moon's attraction is weakest, the sea rises in a second bulge. The gravity attraction of the Sun produces similar but smaller effects: the 'lunar tide' is twice as big as the 'solar tide'.

With the Moon in line with the Sun at new and full moon the solar tide is added to the lunar tide to create the largest tides, called 'spring

*► The lunar component of a sea tide is about twice as large as the solar component, so the observed tide follows the Moon. At new and full moon the solar component, working in line with the Moon, enlarges the lunar component to give spring tides. At first and last quarter the solar component works at 90° to the lunar component, reducing it to neap tides. Tides get bigger towards new and full moon, and get smaller towards first and last quarter.*

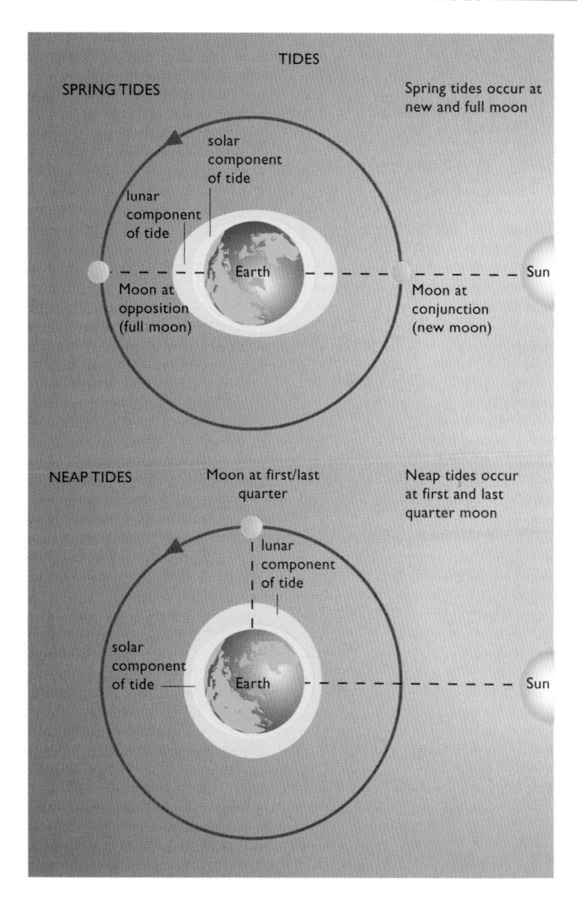


tides'. With the Moon at first and last quarter the solar tide subtracts from the lunar tide to give small 'neap tides'. The time lags involved in moving large volumes of water mean the largest spring tide in a series is experienced on average three tides after astronomical new and full moons.

At any one seaport the high tide is experienced when the Moon is a particular approximate angular distance from the meridian. The approximate angle is a constant for the particular port. A simple way of determining the angle is to take note of the position of the Sun at high tide on days of new and full moon: there will be a high tide whenever the Moon reaches that same approximate position, and another when it reaches a counterpart and hidden position at 180° distance. Although numerous and complicating factors mean the method cannot be made precise, it remains a useful guide.

## Eclipses

An eclipse of the Sun takes place when the Moon passes directly between the Earth and the Sun. An eclipse of the Moon occurs when the Moon passes through the shadow of the Earth. Solar eclipses therefore take place only at the time of new moon, and lunar eclipses only at the time of full moon.

Because the plane of the Moon's orbit is inclined to the plane of the ecliptic, the Moon at opposition and at conjunction is usually above or below the ecliptic plane. Eclipses can occur only when the Sun is passing a node at the time of opposition or conjunction. This happens every 173.3 days, and there is usually at least one solar and one lunar eclipse near this time.

The Moon's diameter is hundreds of times smaller than the Sun's, so the Moon throws a cone-shaped shadow. Eclipses of the Sun are more common than eclipses of the Moon because the Earth makes a large target; however, the tip of the Moon's shadow tracks over a very small area of the Earth, so total eclipses of the Sun are very rare from any particular place on the Earth's surface.

► *In a total lunar eclipse the Moon remains faintly visible because the Earth's atmosphere acts as a lens to bend a predominantly red light onto the Moon's surface. Here the Moon is seen partly illuminated, partly eclipsed, against a background of stars normally lost in the glare of the full moon.*

▼ *A solar eclipse is observed when the Moon comes directly between the Earth and the Sun.*

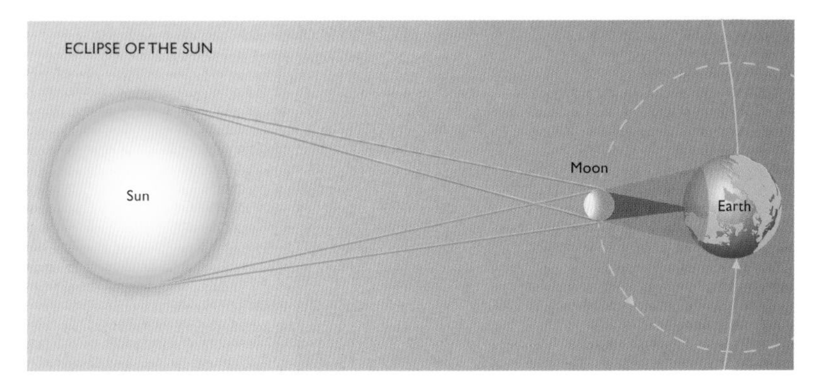

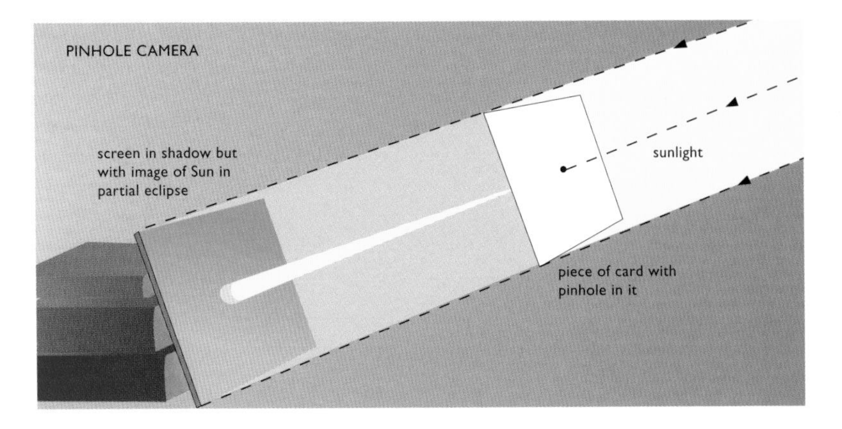


Annular eclipses occur when the distance from the Earth to the Moon is close to maximum (the Moon at apogee) so that the dark Moon is seen surrounded by a disc of sunlight. Partial eclipses, in which only part of the Sun's disc is covered, can be seen from a much larger area of the Earth's surface and are fairly common.

*Looking at the Sun, even through filters, can cause blindness. Eclipses of the Sun can be observed by projecting an image through a pinhole.*

Lunar eclipses are seen when the Moon passes wholly (total eclipse) or partly (partial eclipse) through the Earth's shadow, and are visible from anywhere that has sight of the Moon at the time of the eclipse.

▲ *A pinhole camera is easily constructed from two pieces of card: one is used as the screen, the other has a pinhole to act as the lens.*

▼ *A lunar eclipse is observed when the Earth comes directly between the Sun and the Moon.*

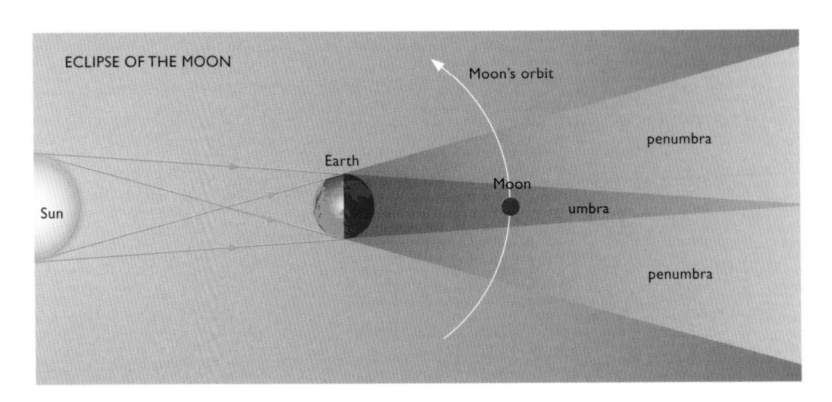

Because the illuminating Sun is larger than the Earth, the area of total shadow thrown by the Earth is a converging cone, called the 'umbra', and the area of partial shadow a diverging fan, the 'penumbra'. At the beginning of a lunar eclipse the Moon moves into the penumbra, but the darkening effect is hard to observe. As the Moon moves into the umbra the Earth's shadow is seen to move across the face of the Moon. In a total eclipse the whole Moon passes into shadow, but remains dimly illuminated in a predominantly red light refracted through the Earth's atmosphere. This effect can be seen in the photograph on page 24.

## ECLIPSES OF THE SUN AND MOON 2005–2025

SUN: ●T: total eclipse; ●P: partial eclipse; ●A: annular eclipse
MOON: ☽T: total eclipse; ☽P: partial eclipse

Date and the approximate time are given as month-day-hour (GMT).
The position of the Rising Node of the Moon (☊) is given for 1st January for each year, expressed in degrees of the ecliptic.

| Year (☊) | Eclipse | Date |
|---|---|---|
| **2005 (☊) 28°** | | |
| | ●A | 10-03-1030 |
| | ☽P | 10-17-1205 |
| **2006 (☊) 9°** | | |
| | ●T | 03-29-1010 |
| | ☽P | 09-07-1850 |
| | ●A | 09-22-1140 |
| **2007 (☊) 350°** | | |
| | ☽T | 03-03-2320 |
| | ●P | 03-19-0230 |
| | ☽T | 08-28-1040 |
| | ●P | 09-11-1230 |
| **2008 (☊) 330°** | | |
| | ●A | 02-07-0355 |
| | ☽T | 02-21-0325 |
| | ●T | 08-01-1020 |
| | ☽P | 08-16-2110 |
| **2009 (☊) 311°** | | |
| | ●A | 01-26-0800 |
| | ●T | 07-22-0235 |
| | ☽P | 12-31-1925 |
| **2010 (☊) 292°** | | |
| | ●A | 01-15-0705 |
| | ☽P | 06-26-1140 |
| | ●T | 07-11-1930 |
| | ☽T | 12-21-0815 |
| **2011 (☊) 272°** | | |
| | ●P | 01-04-0850 |
| | ●P | 06-01-2115 |
| | ☽T | 06-15-2015 |
| | ●P | 07-01-0840 |
| | ●P | 11-25-0620 |
| | ☽T | 12-10-1430 |
| **2012 (☊) 253°** | | |
| | ●A | 05-20-2355 |
| | ☽P | 06-04-1100 |
| | ●T | 11-13-2210 |
| **2013 (☊) 234°** | | |
| | ☽P | 04-25-2005 |
| | ●A | 05-10-0025 |
| | ●T | 11-03-1245 |
| **2014 (☊) 214°** | | |
| | ☽T | 04-15-0745 |
| | ●A | 04-29-0600 |
| | ☽T | 10-08-1055 |
| | ●P | 10-23-2150 |
| **2015 (☊) 195°** | | |
| | ●T | 03-20-0950 |
| | ☽P | 04-04-1200 |
| | ●P | 09-13-0700 |
| | ☽T | 09-28-0245 |
| **2016 (☊) 176°** | | |
| | ●T | 03-09-0200 |
| | ●A | 09-01-0900 |
| **2017 (☊) 156°** | | |
| | ●A | 02-26-1455 |
| | ☽P | 08-07-1820 |
| | ●T | 08-21-1825 |
| **2018 (☊) 137°** | | |
| | ☽T | 01-31-1330 |
| | ●P | 02-15-2055 |
| | ●P | 07-13-0300 |
| | ☽T | 07-27-2020 |
| | ●P | 08-11-0945 |
| **2019 (☊) 118°** | | |
| | ●P | 01-06-0145 |
| | ☽T | 01-21-0510 |
| | ●T | 07-02-1925 |
| | ☽P | 07-16-2130 |
| | ●A | 12-26-0520 |
| **2020 (☊) 98°** | | |
| | ●A | 06-21-0640 |
| | ●T | 12-14-1615 |
| **2021 (☊) 79°** | | |
| | ☽T | 05-26-1120 |
| | ●A | 06-10-1045 |
| | ☽P | 11-19-0905 |
| | ●T | 12-04-0735 |
| **2022 (☊) 60°** | | |
| | ●P | 04-30-2045 |
| | ☽T | 05-16-0410 |
| | ●P | 10-25-1100 |
| | ☽T | 11-08-1100 |
| **2023 (☊) 40°** | | |
| | ●T | 04-20-0420 |
| | ●A | 10-14-1800 |
| | ☽P | 10-28-2015 |
| **2024 (☊) 21°** | | |
| | ●T | 04-08-1820 |
| | ☽P | 09-18-0245 |
| | ●A | 10-02-1845 |
| **2025 (☊) 2°** | | |
| | ☽T | 03-14-0700 |
| | ●P | 03-29-1045 |
| | ☽T | 09-07-1810 |
| | ☽P | 09-21-1940 |

## *Learning to recognize the constellations*

The easiest way to learn your way around the stars is to identify particular constellations and to use those as a key to finding the rest. Such 'key' constellations can be found in two directions, looking towards the poles, and looking towards the equator.

The equatorial maps in this atlas show the area of sky that passes through the meridian around local midnight each month (the centre of each map passes the meridian on or about the 20th of the month). Local midnight is exactly halfway between sunset and sunrise (see sundial time, page 10); sundial time is not the same thing as civil time, which is based on time zones and usually pretends that midnight is an hour or two earlier than it is. When observing before midnight refer to the map for an earlier month, even two or three months earlier, as necessary. Each map overlaps with the next, and it takes a run of up to six maps to show the whole sky open to view at any one time, east to west.

The maps are drawn to a very small scale and the user should bear this in mind when relating the maps to the very large scale of the sky. One side of a map to the other represents 68°, top to bottom represents 120°.

Looking with one eye at a hand held at arm's length gives a rough measure of angular size in the sky: a thumbnail covers 2°, a clenched fist spans 9–10°, a handspan (thumb to tip of little finger with the fingers spread) covers about 20°.

### *Looking towards the poles*

For observers in temperate latitudes of the northern hemisphere the key constellations are Ursa Major, Ursa Minor and Cassiopeia. The main stars of Ursa Major form the shape of a ladle, and in America this group is known as the Big Dipper. In Britain it is known as the Plough. An imaginary line drawn through Merak and Dubhe (β and α UMa) leads to Polaris (α UMi), the Pole Star. Cassiopeia is found on the other side of the pole from Ursa Major, and looks like a giant W or M, depending on the angle.

The region around the south celestial pole has no bright stars in it, so there is no convenient pole star in the southern sky for observers in the southern hemisphere. The best-known group in the southern sky is Crux, the Southern Cross. Crux is circumpolar from southern Australia and most of New Zealand. Fifteen degrees of arc – less than a handspan – east of Crux is the bright pair Agena and Rigil Kent (β and α Cen), 5° apart. Crux and these two stars stand 30° to one side of the celestial pole, while Achernar (α Eri) stands 30° to the other side. The solitary bright star Canopus (α Car) also stands a similar distance away from the pole, halfway along the arc separating Achernar from Crux (see the diagram on page 9).

### *Northern hemisphere, looking south*

In winter (December onwards, Equatorial Map 9) the key group is Orion. NW of Orion are the Pleiades, a smudgy-looking cluster of stars, and the orange star Aldebaran, the eye of the Bull (Taurus). The Pleaides and Hyades are both open star clusters and make fine binocular objects. Sirius, the brightest star in the sky, rises in the SE.

In spring (March onwards, Equatorial Maps 5 and 6) Leo (containing the bright bluish star Regulus) rises high through the southern sky, with Ursa Major above it on the same side of the pole. Continuing the handle of Ursa Major down in a curve leads to Arcturus, the orange-yellow star in Boötes.

In summer (June onwards, Equatorial Map 3) the blue-green star Vega becomes prominent, rising to zenith through east. Arcturus (Equatorial Map 5) has passed the meridian, and Corona Borealis lies between. The red star Antares (in Scorpius) is low on the southern horizon.

In late summer (July through September) find the large-scale grouping known as the Summer Triangle (Equatorial Map 2): Vega (in Lyra), Deneb (in Cygnus) and Altair (in Aquila).

In autumn (September onwards, Equatorial Map 12) the key group is the Square of Pegasus. The Summer Triangle stays visible until the beginning of winter.

### *Southern hemisphere, looking north*

*View the maps upside down!*

In summer (December onwards, Equatorial Map 9) the key grouping is Orion, with the bright star Sirius above it to the east.

In autumn Regulus (Equatorial Map 6) is sinking towards the west; Corvus approaches the zenith at midnight, with blue-green Spica (Virgo) following.

In winter (June onwards, Equatorial Map 3) the key star is red Antares in Scorpius seen towards the zenith, with the rich starfields of Sagittarius following.

In spring (September onwards, Equatorial Map 12) the key star Fomalhaut (α PsA) is close to the zenith. Fomalhaut heads a giant V (Equatorial Map 12): 28° NE is Deneb Kaitos (β Cet), 23° SE is Ankaa (α Phe), and 20° SE of Ankaa is Achernar (α Eri).

## *The constellation names*

When the constellation name follows a star's name, letter or number, the genitive form of the name is used, thus: Deneb Cygni, α Cygni, 50 Cygni. Abbreviations of the constellation names (or rather, of their genitive forms) are increasingly used in printed references to stars: for example, α Cyg.

| THE CONSTELLATION NAMES | | | |
|---|---|---|---|
| Abbr. | Name | Genitive | English form |
| And | Andromeda | Andromedae | Andromeda |
| Ant | Antlia | Antliae | The Air Pump |
| Aps | Apus | Apodis | The Bird of Paradise |
| Aqr | Aquarius | Aquarii | The Water Carrier |
| Aql | Aquila | Aquiliae | The Eagle |
| Ara | Ara | Arae | The Altar |
| Ari | Aries | Arietis | The Ram |
| Aur | Auriga | Aurigae | The Charioteer |
| Boo | Boötes | Boötis | The Herdsman |
| Cae | Caelum | Caeli | The Graving Tool |
| Cam | Camelopardalis | Camelopardalis | The Giraffe |
| Cnc | Cancer | Cancri | The Crab |
| CVn | Canes Venatici | Canum Venaticorum | The Hunting Dogs |
| CMa | Canis Major | Canis Majoris | The Greater Dog |
| CMi | Canis Minor | Canis Minoris | The Lesser Dog |
| Cap | Carpricornus | Capricorni | The Sea Goat |
| Car | Carina | Carinae | The Keel |
| Cas | Cassiopeia | Cassiopeiae | Cassiopeia |
| Cen | Centaurus | Centauri | The Centaur |
| Cep | Cepheus | Cephei | Cepheus |
| Cet | Cetus | Ceti | The Whale |
| Cha | Chamaeleon | Chamaeleontis | The Chamaeleon |
| Cir | Circinus | Circini | The Compasses |
| Col | Columba | Columbae | The Dove |
| Com | Coma Berenices | Comae Berenicis | Berenice's Hair |
| CrA | Corona Australis | Coronae Australis | The Southern Crown |
| CrB | Corona Borealis | Coronae Borealis | The Northern Crown |
| Crv | Corvus | Corvi | The Crow |
| Crt | Crater | Crateris | The Cup |
| Cru | Crux Australis | Crucis | The Southern Cross |
| Cyg | Cygnus | Cygni | The Swan |
| Del | Delphinus | Delphini | The Dolphin |
| Dor | Dorado | Doradus | The Swordfish |
| Dra | Draco | Draconis | The Dragon |
| Equ | Equuleus | Equulei | The Little Horse |
| Eri | Eridanus | Eridani | The River Eridanus |
| For | Fornax | Fornacis | The Furnace |
| Gem | Gemini | Geminorum | The Twins |
| Gru | Grus | Gruis | The Crane |
| Her | Hercules | Herculis | Hercules |
| Hor | Horologium | Horologii | The Pendulum Clock |
| Hya | Hydra | Hydrae | The Water Snake |
| Hyi | Hydrus | Hydri | The Lesser Water Snake |
| Ind | Indus | Indi | The Indian |
| Lac | Lacerta | Lacertae | The Lizard |

| Leo | Leo | Leonis | The Lion |
|---|---|---|---|
| LMi | Leo Minor | Leonis Minoris | The Smaller Lion |
| Lep | Lepus | Leporis | The Hare |
| Lib | Libra | Librae | The Scales |
| Lup | Lupus | Lupi | The Wolf |
| Lyn | Lynx | Lyncis | The Lynx |
| Lyr | Lyra | Lyrae | The Lyre |
| Men | Mensa | Mensae | The Table Mountain |
| Mic | Microscopium | Microscopii | The Microscope |
| Mon | Monoceros | Monocerotis | The Unicorn |
| Mus | Musca | Muscae | The Fly |
| Nor | Norma | Normae | The Level |
| Oct | Octans | Octantis | The Octant |
| Oph | Ophiuchus | Ophiuchi | The Serpent Holder |
| Ori | Orion | Orionis | Orion |
| Pav | Pavo | Pavonis | The Peacock |
| Peg | Pegasus | Pegasi | Pegasus |
| Per | Perseus | Persei | Perseus |
| Phe | Phoenix | Phoenicis | The Phoenix |
| Pic | Pictor | Pictoris | The Painter |
| Pic | Pisces | Piscium | The Fishes |
| PsA | Piscis Austrinus | Piscis Austrini | The Southern Fish |
| Pup | Puppis | Puppis | The Stern |
| Pyx | Pyxis | Pyxidis | The Mariner's Compass |
| Ret | Reticulum | Reticuli | The Net |
| Sge | Sagitta | Sagittae | The Arrow |
| Sgr | Sagittarius | Sagittarii | The Archer |
| Sco | Scorpius | Scorpii | The Scorpion |
| Scl | Sculptor | Sculptoris | The Sculptor |
| Sct | Scutum | Scuti | The Shield |
| Ser | Serpens* | Serpentis | The Serpent |
| Sex | Sextans | Sextantis | The Sextant |
| Tau | Taurus | Tauri | The Bull |
| Tel | Telescopium | Telescopii | The Telescope |
| Tri | Triangulum | Trianguli | The Triangle |
| TrA | Triangulum Australe | Triangulum Australis | The Southern Triangle |
| Tuc | Tucana | Tucanae | The Toucan |
| UMa | Ursa Major | Ursae Majoris | The Great Bear |
| UMi | Ursa Minor | Ursae Minoris | The Little Bear |
| Vel | Vela | Velorum | The Sails |
| Vir | Virgo | Virginis | The Virgin |
| Vol | Volans | Volantis | The Flying Fish |
| Vul | Vulpecula | Vulpeculae | The Little Fox |

**The constellation of Serpens has been sectioned in two parts, which are sometimes denoted separately:*

| SerCp | Serpens Caput | Serpentis Caput | The Serpent's Head |
|---|---|---|---|
| SerCd | Serpens Cauda | Serpentis Cauda | The Serpent's Tail |

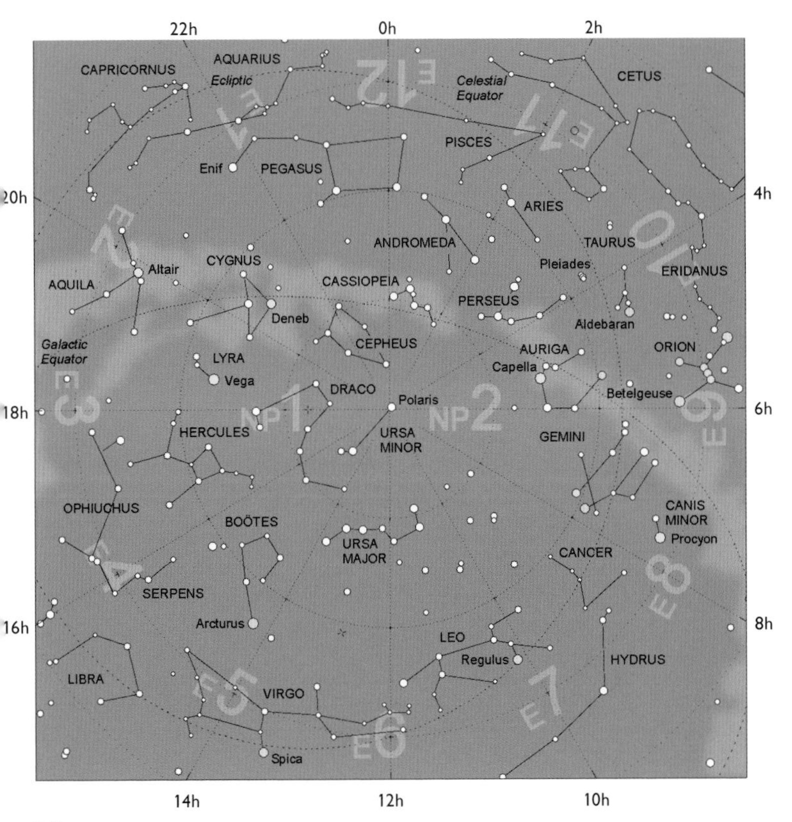


## The maps

The map series begins with a Northern Sky map showing the constellations of the northern sky with the north celestial pole at the centre, and with the celestial equator in a circle towards the edge of the map. A Southern Sky map is found at the end of the series.

The series continues with a pair of maps showing the northern sky, and ends with a pair of maps showing the southern. For observers in temperate latitudes, stars on one or other of these maps will be circumpolar. The equatorial map series shows the stars of the central sky, including the stars of the ecliptic, in 12 maps. Each shows the sky passing through the meridian around local midnight in one of the months of the year. In any night each map replaces the next every two hours. If observing before midnight, start with the map for an earlier month.

Stars brighter than magnitude 2 are shown colour tinted according to spectral type. In the case of orange to red K to M types, this reflects colour visible to the naked eye. The key to the maps appears on page 48.

Left side in overlapping pair

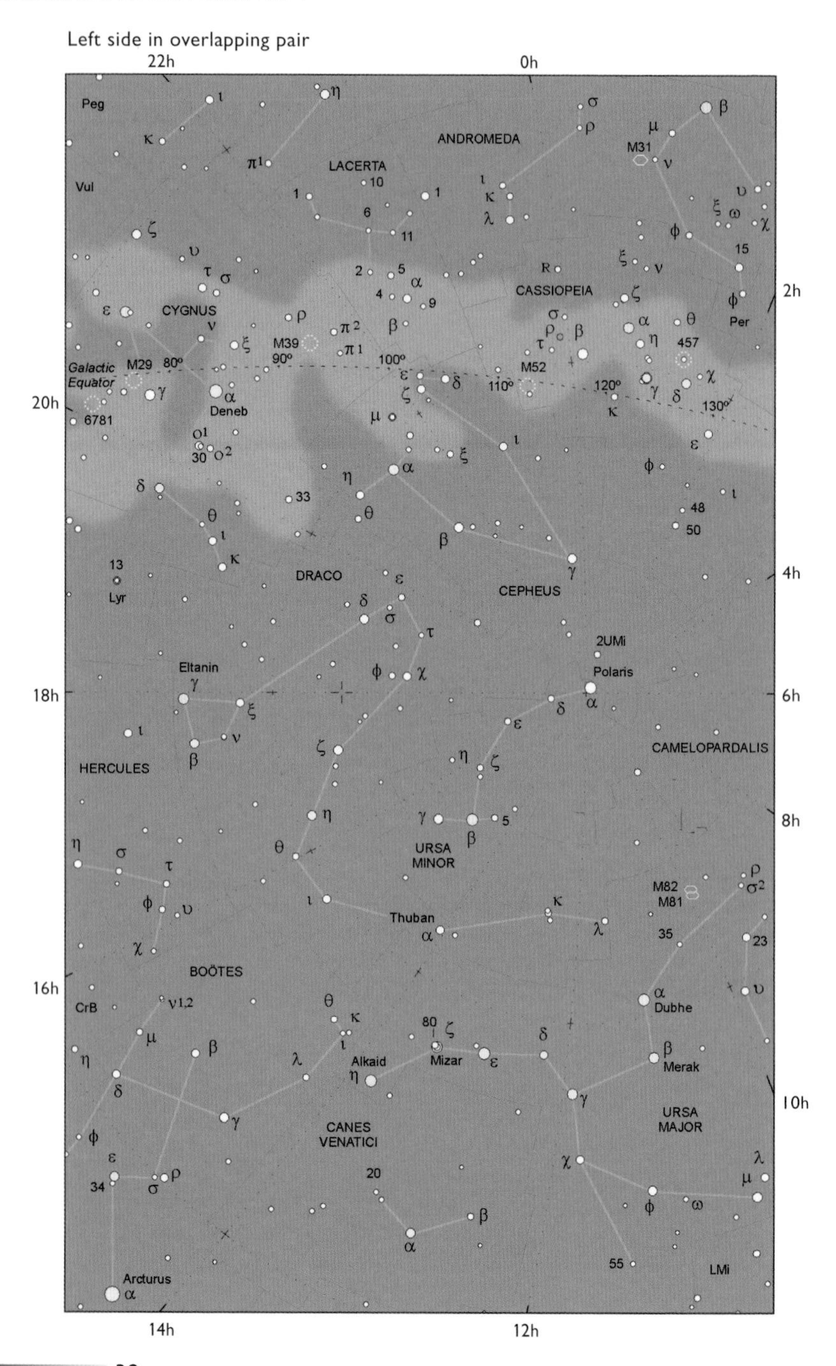

Right side in overlapping pair

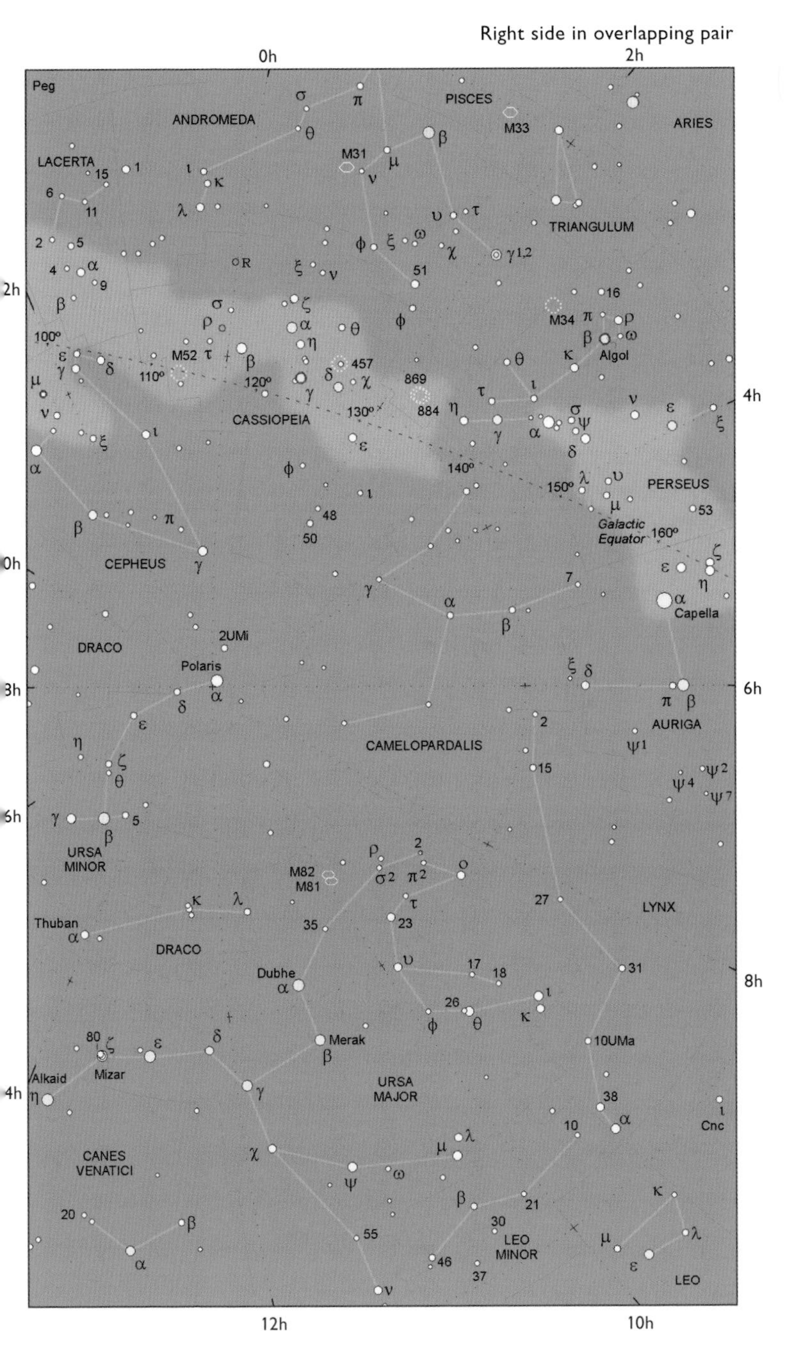

The map shows the night sky on the meridian at local midnight in August

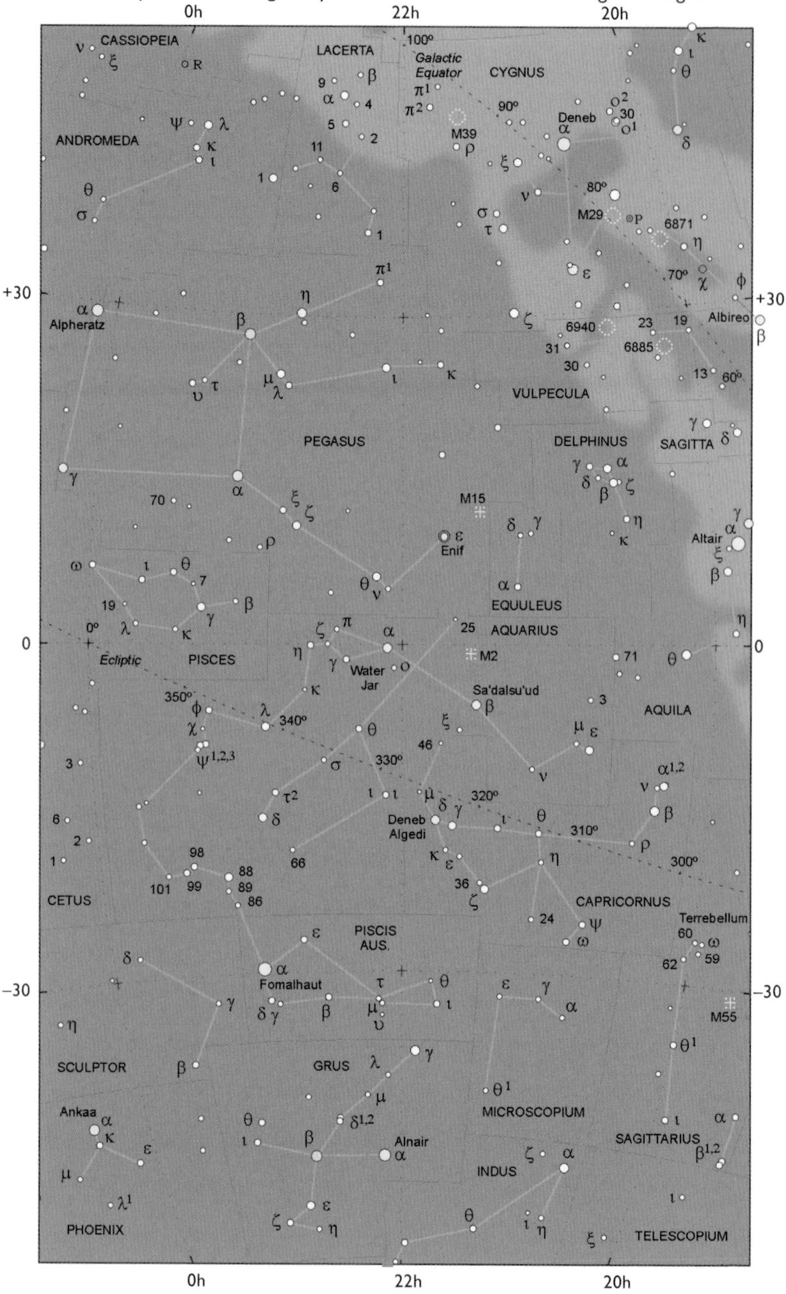

The map shows the night sky on the meridian at local midnight in July

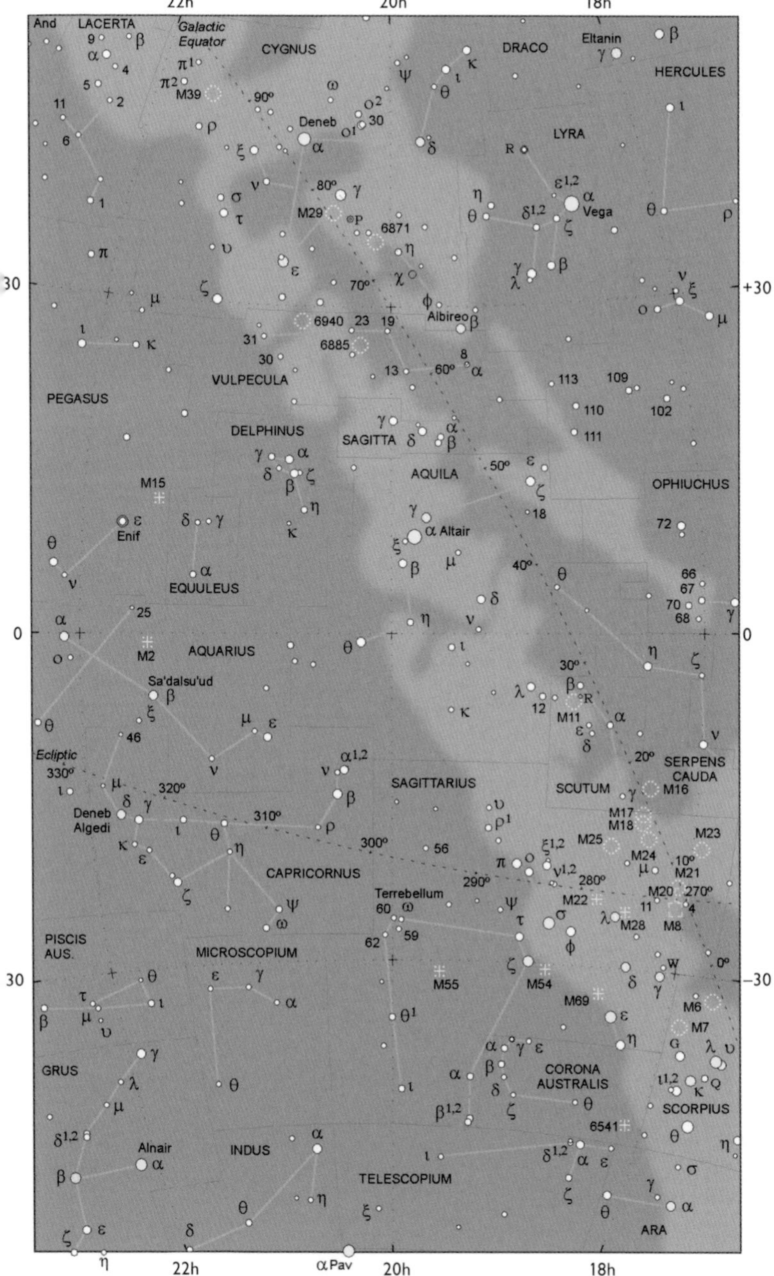

The map shows the night sky on the meridian at local midnight in June

The map shows the night sky on the meridian at local midnight in May

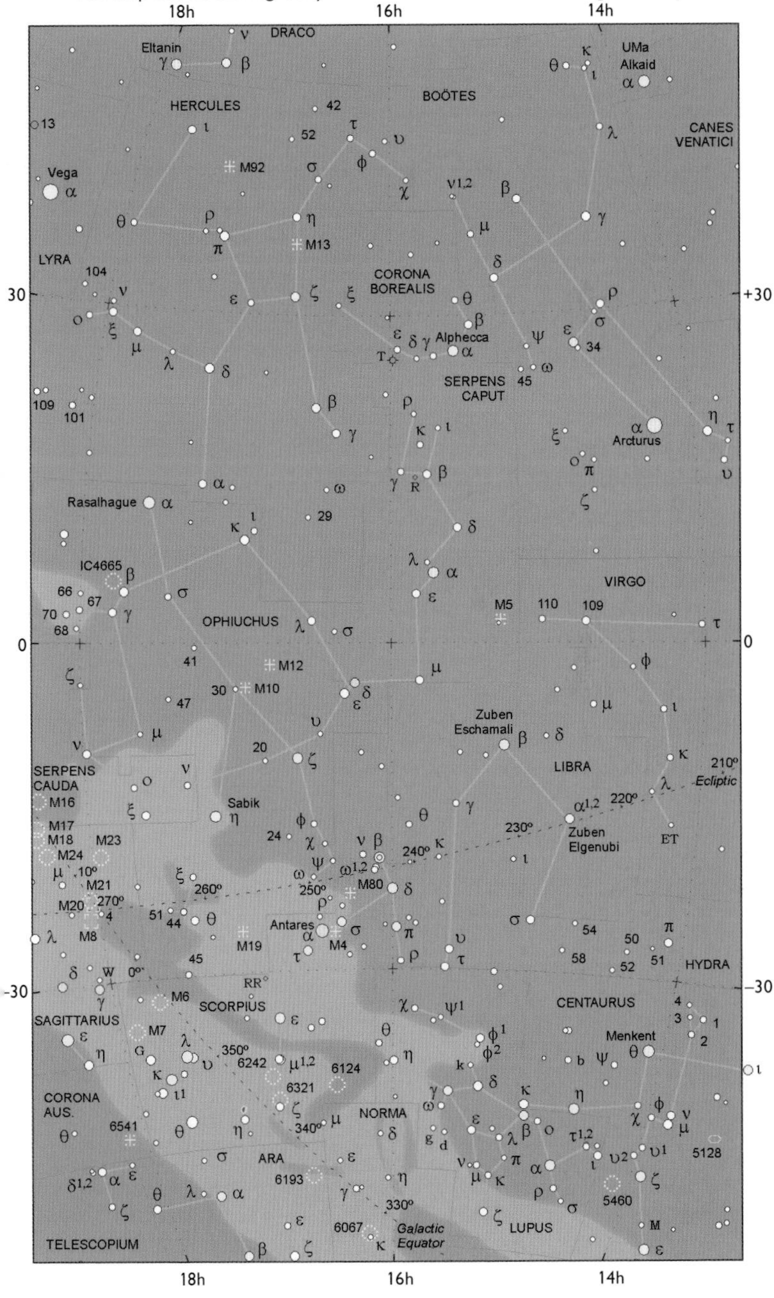

18h 16h 14h

+30

0

−30

18h 16h 14h

The map shows the night sky on the meridian at local midnight in April

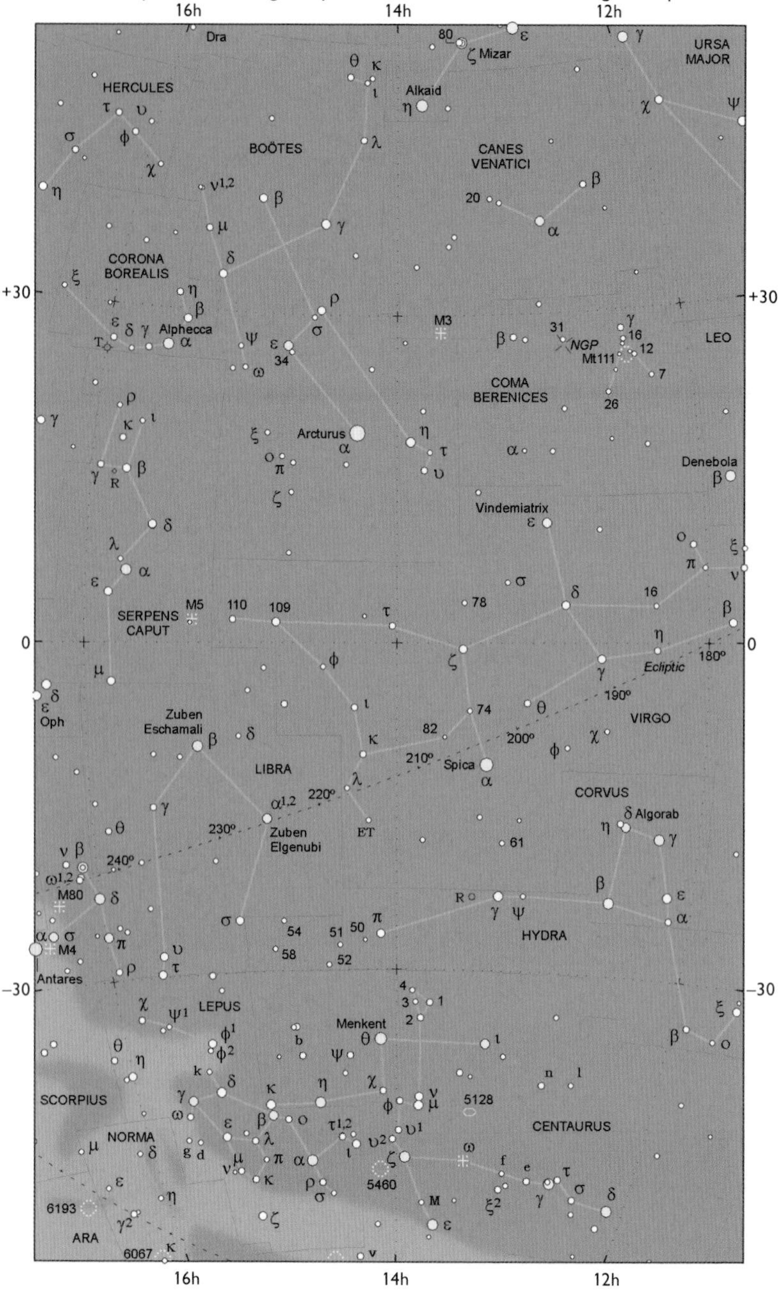

16h 14h 12h

Dra
Mizar
URSA MAJOR
HERCULES
Alkaid
BOÖTES
CANES VENATICI
CORONA BOREALIS
Alphecca
M3
NGP
Mt111
LEO
COMA BERENICES
Arcturus
Denebola
Vindemiatrix
SERPENS CAPUT
M5
Ecliptic
Oph
Zuben Eschamali
VIRGO
LIBRA
Spica
CORVUS
Algorab
Zuben Elgenubi
M80
HYDRA
M4
Antares
LEPUS
Menkent
SCORPIUS
5128
CENTAURUS
NORMA
5460
6193
ARA
6067

+30 0 −30

16h 14h 12h

The map shows the night sky on the meridian at local midnight in March

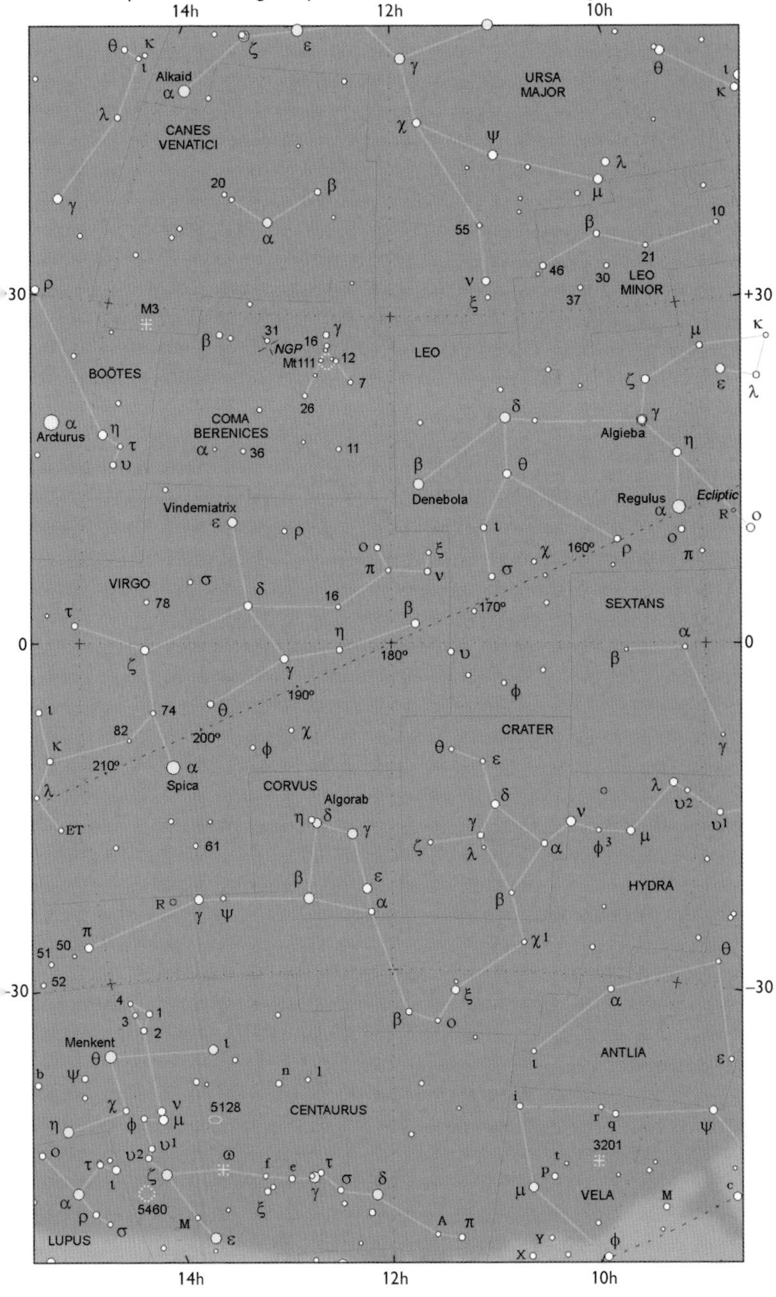

The map shows the night sky on the meridian at local midnight in February

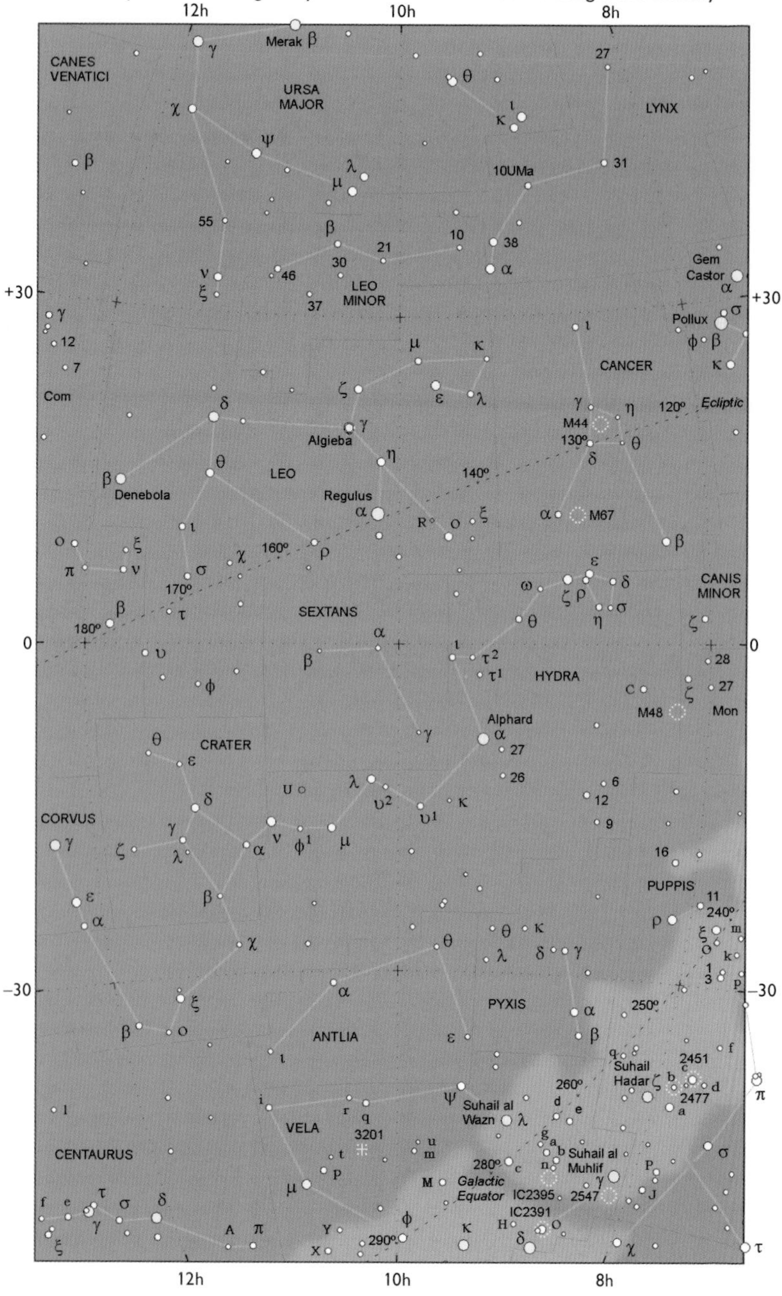

The map shows the night sky on the meridian at local midnight in January

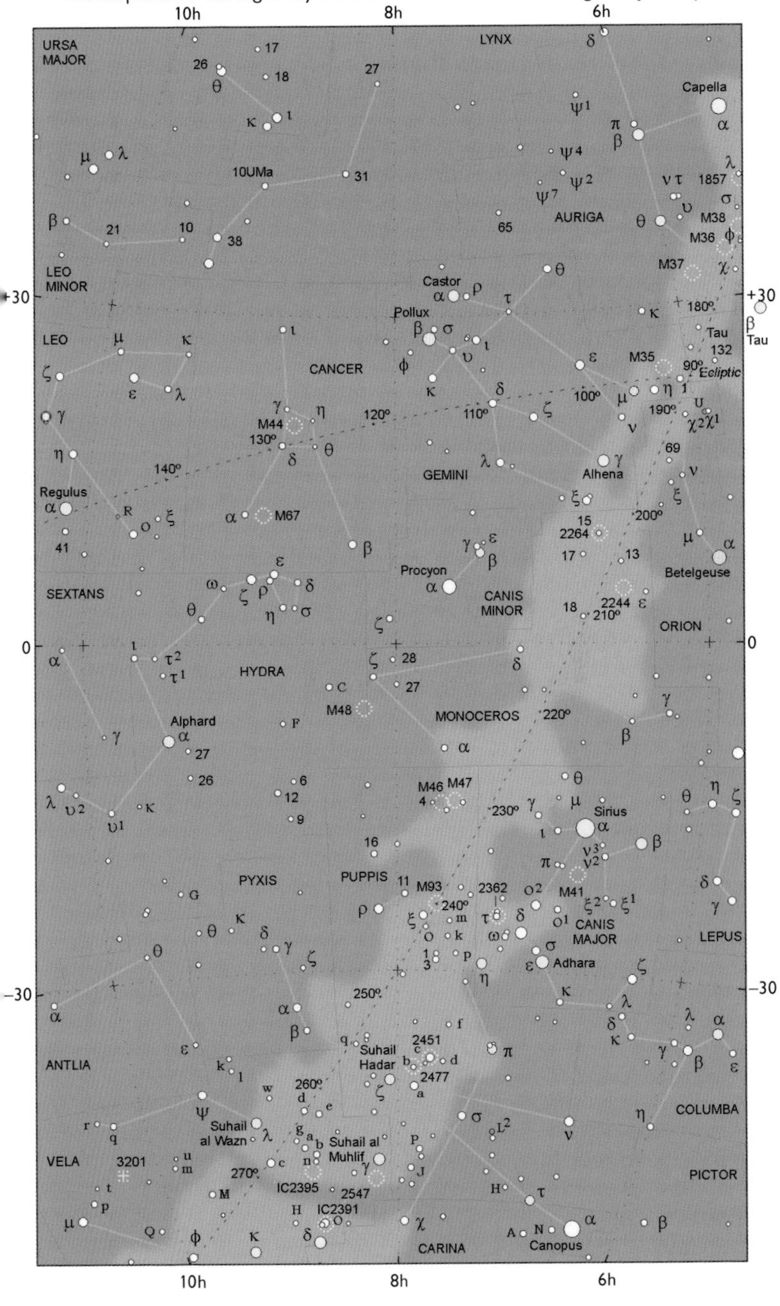

The map shows the night sky on the meridian at local midnight in December

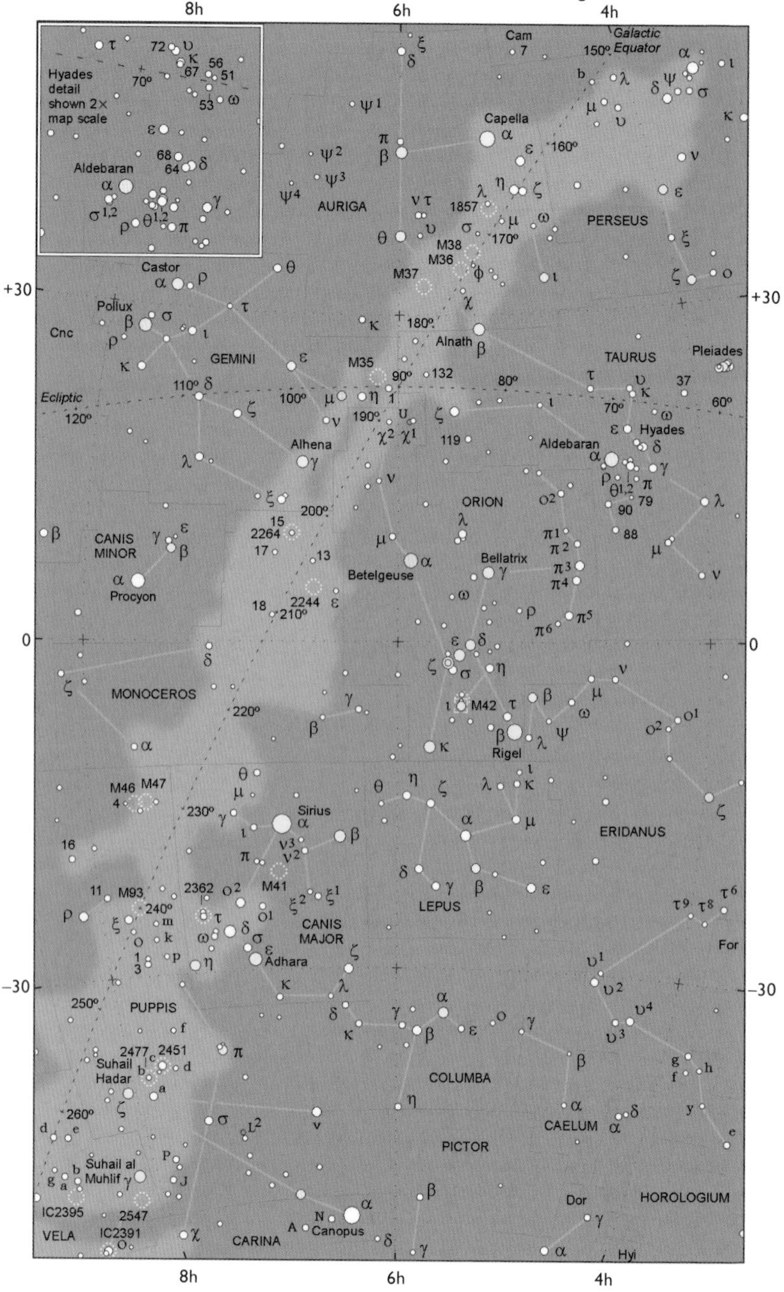

The map shows the night sky on the meridian at local midnight in November

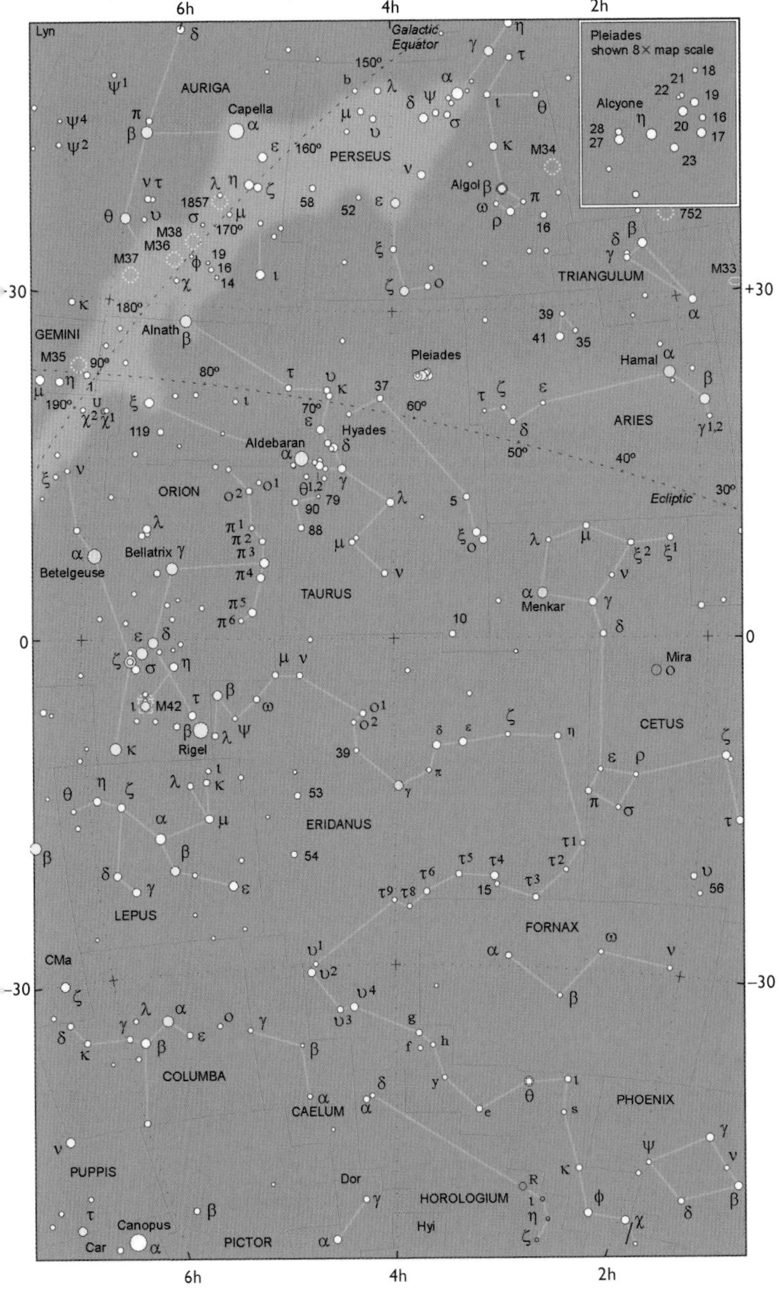

The map shows the night sky on the meridian at local midnight in October

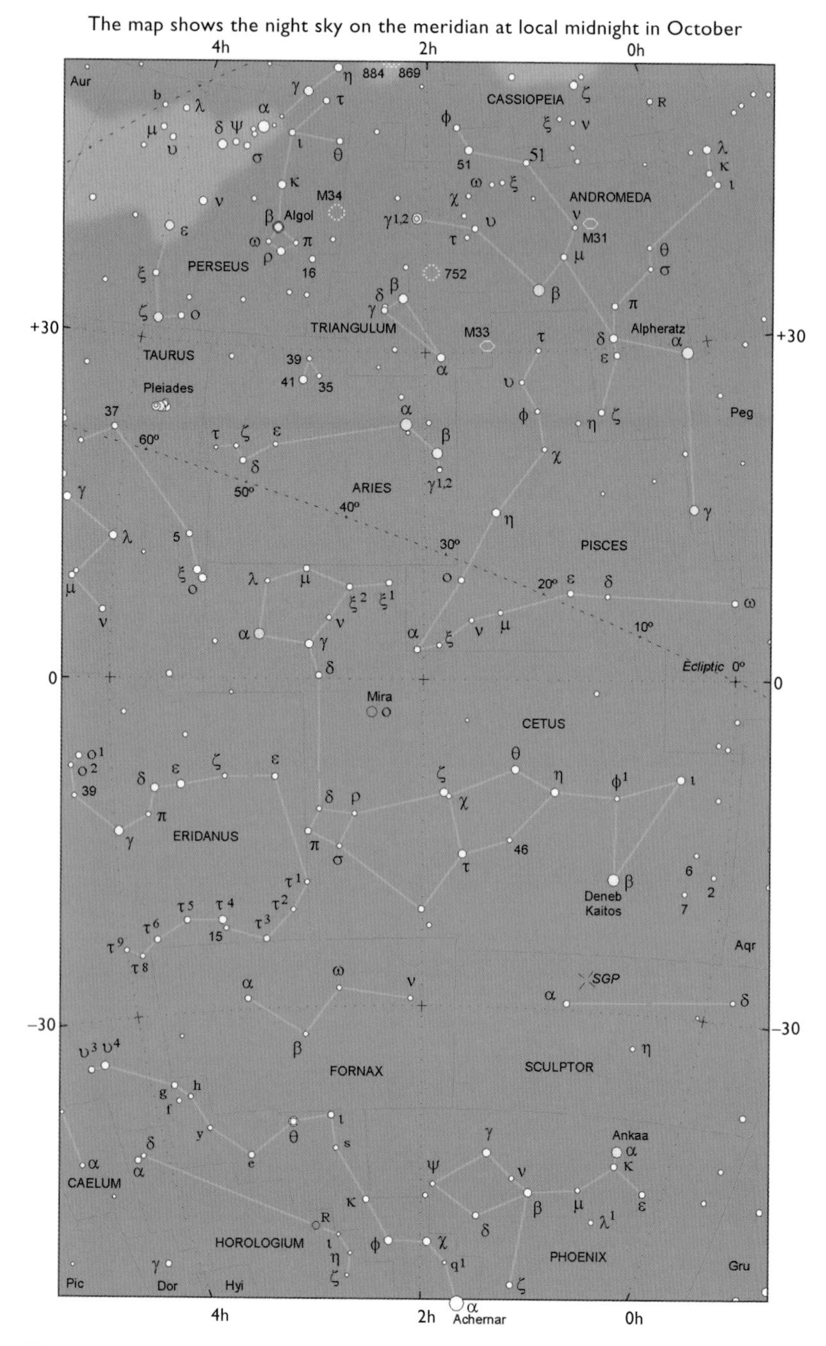

The map shows the night sky on the meridian at local midnight in September

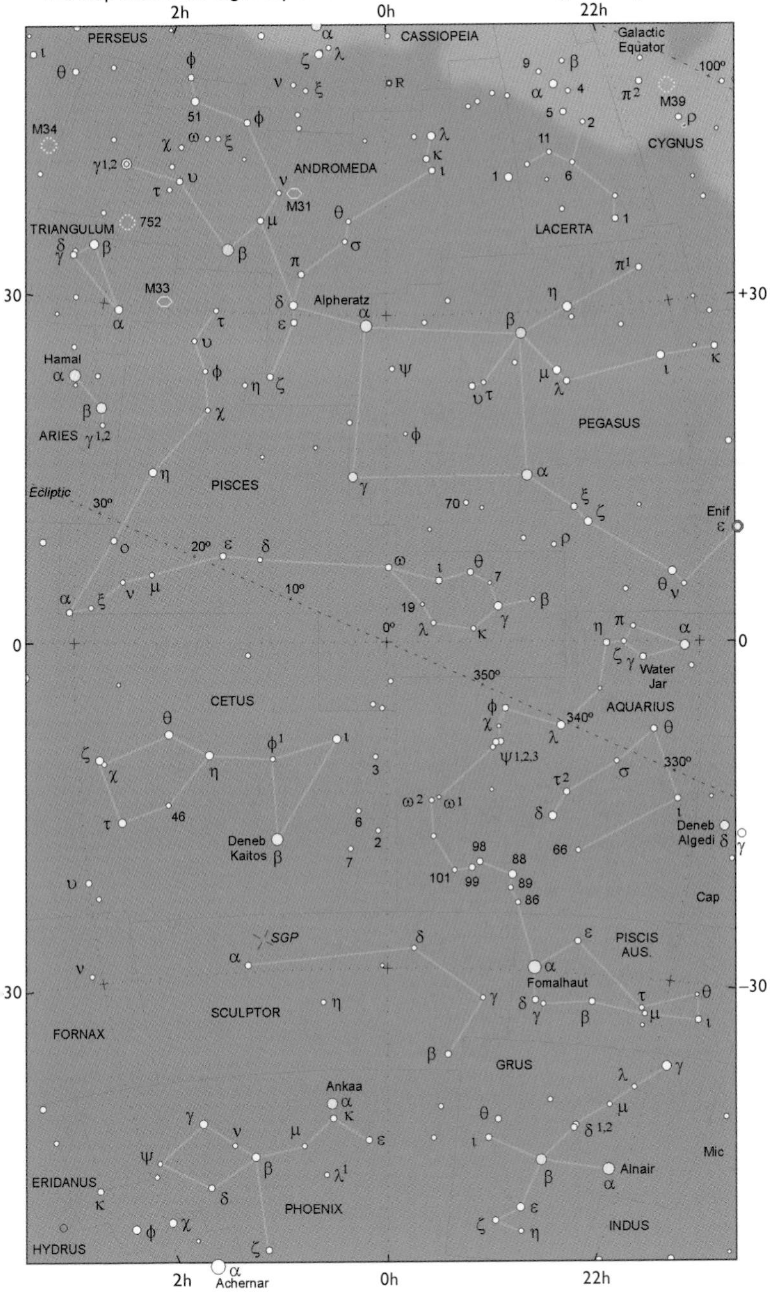

Left side in overlapping pair

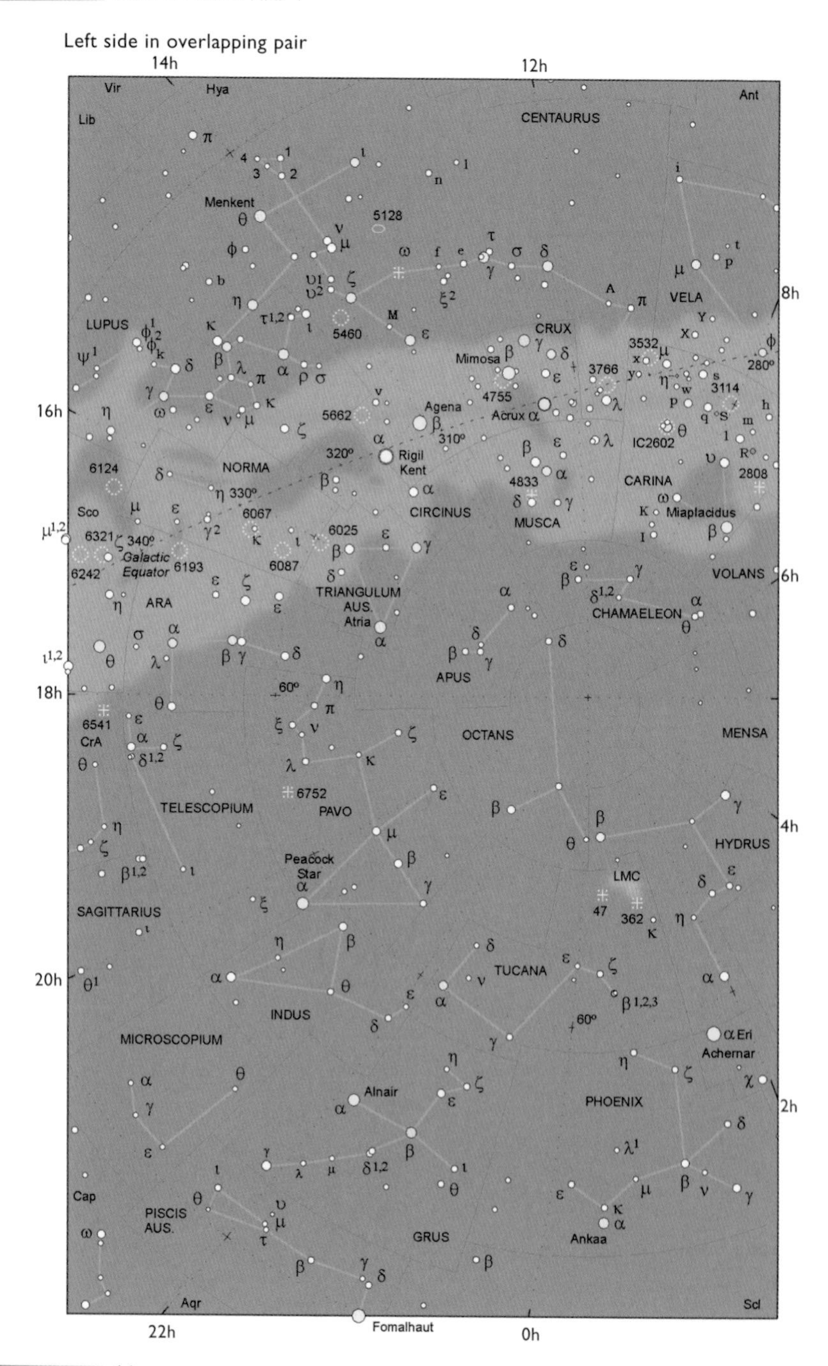

Right side in overlapping pair

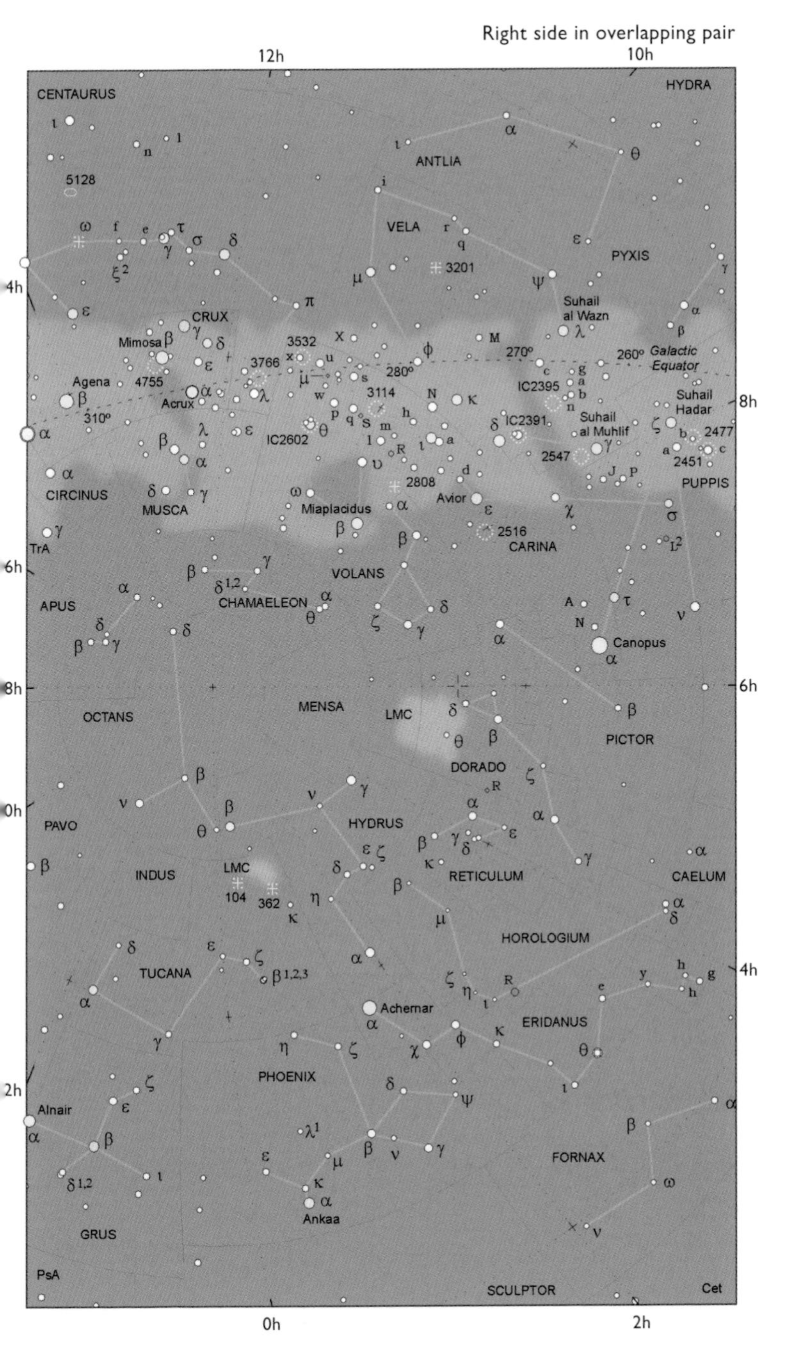

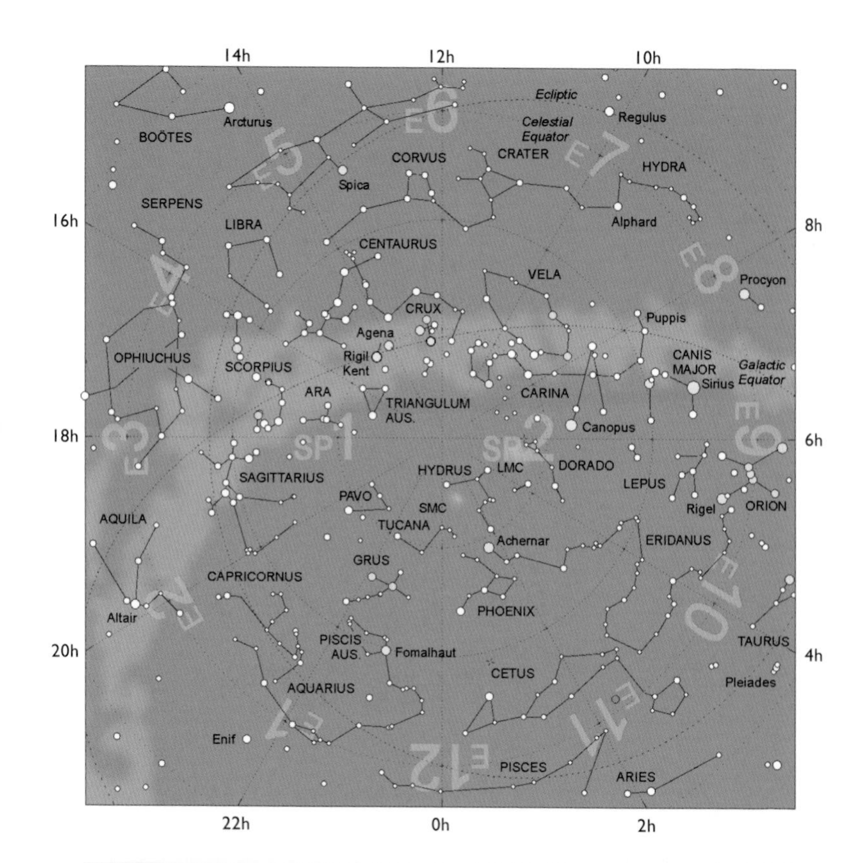


## KEY TO MAIN MAP SERIES

0 1 2 3 4 5 stars, apparent visual magnitude

variable star

open cluster

diffuse nebula

variable star, naked-eye visible only at maximum

globular cluster

external galaxy

NGP = North Galactic Pole

SGP = South Galactic Pole

## LOWER CASE GREEK ALPHABET USED FOR DESIGNATING STARS

| | | | | | |
|---|---|---|---|---|---|
| α alpha | κ kappa | τ tau | ϵ epsilon | ξ xi | ψ psi |
| ι iota | σ sigma | δ delta | ν nu | χ chi | θ theta |
| ρ rho | γ gamma | μ mu | ϕ phi | η eta | π pi |
| β beta | λ lambda | υ upsilon | ζ zeta | ο omicron | ω omega |

### *The brightest stars*

The table lists 27 stars brighter than visual magnitude 2.0. A double entry under 'spectrum' (for example, G2V + K1V) gives the spectrum of the two major components of a multiple system (list shows combined magnitude). Under 'notes', m represents a multiple system, with the number of members given in brackets, v represents variable. A brief description of spectral type can be found on pages 16–17.

THE BRIGHTEST STARS

| Name | Desig. | Visual mag. | Spectrum | Absolute mag. | Dist. ly | Notes |
|---|---|---|---|---|---|---|
| Sun | Sol | –26.74 | G2V | +4.83 | — | — |
| Sirius | α CMa | –1.46 | A1Vm | 1.4 | 8.8 | m(4) |
| Canopus | α Car | –0.72 | F0Ib | –4.7 | 200 | — |
| Rigil Kent | $\alpha^{1,2}$ Cen | –0.27 | G2V + K1V | — | 4.25 | m(3) |
| Arcturus | α Boo | –0.04 | K2IIIp | –0.3 | 36 | — |
| Vega | α Lyr | 0.03 | A0V | 0.5 | 26 | m(4) |
| Capella | α Aur | 0.08 | G5IIIe + G0III | — | 46 | m(10) |
| Rigel | β Ori | 0.12 | B8Ia | –7.4 | 1050 | m(4) |
| Procyon | α CMi | 0.34 | F5IV–V | 2.6 | 11.5 | m(5) |
| Achernar | α Eri | 0.46 | B3Vpe | –1.7 | 90 | — |
| Betelgeuse | α Ori | 0.50 | M1–2Ia–be | — | 420 | m(6),v |
| Agena | β Cen | 0.60 | B1III | –4.7 | 360 | m(2) |
| Altair | α Aql | 0.77 | A7IV–V | — | 17 | m(3) |
| Aldebaran | α Tau | 0.85 | K5III | –0.7 | 70 | m(6) |
| Acrux | $\alpha^{1,2}$ Cru | 0.87 | B0.5IV + B1V | — | 520 | m(3) |
| Antares | α Sco | 0.96 | M1.5Ia –Ib + B4Ve | — | 600 | m(2),v |
| Spica | β Vir | 0.98 | B1III–IV + B2V | — | 520 | m(3) |
| Pollux | β Gem | 1.14 | K0III | 1.0 | 6 | m(7) |
| Fomalhaut | α PsA | 1.16 | A3V | 2.0 | 22 | — |
| Mimosa | β Cru | 1.20 | B0.5III | –5.0 | 490 | m(3),v |
| Deneb | α Cyg | 1.25 | A2Ia | –7.5 | 1650 | m(2) |
| Regulus | α Leo | 1.35 | B7V | –0.7 | 90 | m(4) |
| Adhara | ε CMa | 1.50 | B2II | –4.4 | 490 | m(3),v |
| Castor | α Gem | 1.58 | A1V + A2V | — | 50 | m(4) |
| Gacrux | γ Cru | 1.63 | M3II | –0.9 | 105 | m(3) |
| Shaula | λ Sco | 1.63 | B2IV + B | — | 180 | m(3) |
| Bellatrix | β Ori | 1.64 | B2III | –3.6 | 360 | m(2) |
| Al Nath | β Tau | 1.65 | B7III | –1.6 | 150 | m(2) |
| Alnilam | ε Ori | 1.70 | B0Iae | –6.2 | 1200 | m(2) |
| Miaplacidus | β Car | 1.70 | A2IV | –0.6 | 55 | — |
| Alnair | α Gru | 1.74 | B7IV | — | 80 | m(2) |
| Alnitak | ζ Ori | 1.75 | B0III + 09.5Ib | — | 1000 | m(4) |
| Alioth | ε UMa | 1.77 | A0p | — | — | v |
| Suhail Muhlif | γ Vel | 1.78 | WR8 + O7.5e | — | 1500 | m(5) |
| Mirfak | α Per | 1.79 | F5Ib | –4.6 | 620 | m(2) |
| Dubhe | α UMa | 1.79 | K0III | 0.2 | 86 | m(2) |
| Suhail Muhlif | γ Vel | 1.98 | WR8 + O7.5e | — | 1500 | m(5) |

## *Variable stars*

Variable stars are stars whose brightness (listed as apparent magnitude) varies over time. This variation may take place in a regular, semiregular, irregular, or completely unpredictable way. Intrinsic variables (the supreme example is Mira, ο Cet) are variable because of instability or cyclical fuel economics. Some intrinsic variables are of one spectral type/luminosity class at maximum and of another at minimum. In the table both are shown, separated by a dash. Extrinsic (eclipsing) variables (such as Algol, β Per) are multiple systems in which one member periodically eclipses another. In the table the period of variation is shown in days (average periods in italics). Codes used to describe spectral particularities are listed on page 18.

| VARIABLE STARS | | | | | |
|---|---|---|---|---|---|
| Name | Max. | Min. | Period | Spectrum | Variability type |
| η Aql | 3.48 | 4.39 | 7.2 | F6Ib–G4Ib | Cepheid type |
| η Car | –0.8 | 7.9 | — | pec | eruptive (S Dor type) |
| R Car | 3.9 | 10.5 | 309 | M4e–M8e | pulsating (Mira type) |
| S Car | 4.5 | 9.9 | 150 | K5e–M6e | pulsating (Mira type) |
| ρ Cas | 4.1 | 6.2 | *320* | F8Ia–K0Ia–o | semiregular pulsating |
| γ Cas | 1.6 | 3.0 | — | B0.5IVpe | irregular eruptive |
| R Cas | 4.7 | 13.5 | 430 | M6e–M10e | pulsating (Mira type) |
| μ Cep | 3.43 | 5.1 | *730* | M2eIa | semiregular pulsating |
| ο Cet | 2.0 | 10.0 | 332 | M5e–M9e | pulsating (Mira type) |
| T CrB | 2.0 | 10.8 | — | M3III+pec | recurrent nova |
| χ Cyg | 3.3 | 14.2 | 408 | S6.2e–S10.4e | pulsating (Mira type) |
| P Cyg | 3 | 6 | — | B1Iapeq | eruptive (S Dor type) |
| R Dor | 4.8 | 6.6 | *388* | M8IIIe | semiregular pulsating |
| R Dor | 4.8 | 6.6 | 338 | M8IIIe | semiregular pulsating |
| α Her | 2.74 | 4.0 | — | M5Ib–II | semiregular pulsating |
| R Hor | 4.7 | 14.3 | 408 | M5e–M8eII–III | pulsating (Mira type) |
| R Leo | 4.4 | 11.3 | 310 | M6e–M9.5IIIe | pulsating (Mira type) |
| δ Lib | 4.91 | 5.90 | 2.33 | A0IV–V | eclipsing (Algol) |
| β Lyr | 3.25 | 4.36 | 12.9 | B8II–IIIep | eclipsing |
| R Lyr | 3.88 | 5.0 | 46 | M5III | semiregular pulsating |
| α Ori | 0.0 | 1.3 | *2335* | M1–M2Ia–Ibe | semiregular pulsating |
| U Ori | 4.8 | 13.0 | 368 | M6e–M9.5e | pulsating (Mira type) |
| ϵ Peg | 0.7 | 3.5 | — | K2Ib | slow irregular pulsating |
| β Per | 2.12 | 3.39 | 2.87 | B8V | eclipsing (Algol) |
| ζ Pho | 3.91 | 4.42 | 1.67 | B6V+B9V | eclipsing (Algol) |
| $L^2$ Pup | 2.6 | 6.2 | 141 | M5IIIe–M6IIIe | semiregular pulsating |
| R Sct | 4.2 | 8.6 | 147 | G0Iae–K2pIbe | pulsating (RV Tau type) |
| R Ser | 5.16 | 14.4 | 356 | M5IIIe–M9e | pulsating (Mira type) |
| RR Sco | 5.0 | 12.4 | 281 | M6II–IIIe–M9 | pulsating (Mira type) |
| W Sgr | 4.29 | 5.14 | 7.595 | F4–G2Ib | Cepheid type |

## *Double stars*

The table is mostly of stars that can be separated by the naked eye or in a pair of binoculars. Separation is given in minutes of arc. Double and multiple stars are more easily separated where the components are of an equal brightness, and easier for an observer with keen sight.

The present table ranges from wide optical doubles up to 900″ in separation down to telescope doubles separated by 50″ or less. Observers are likely to need binoculars or a telescope to distinguish two stars separated by less than 400″. A good pair of binoculars should be able to separate most of the double stars listed below.

The brighter of two stars in a pair is listed first. PA stands for position angle, the direction of the fainter star measured from the brighter, direction N = 0° through E = 90°.

| DOUBLE STARS | | | | | | |
|---|---|---|---|---|---|---|
| Star/stars | Mag. | Mag. | Spectrum | Spectrum | Separation | PA |
| δ Aps | 4.7 | 5.1 | M5 | M1 | 103″ | 012° |
| $\alpha^1$, $\alpha^2$ Cap<br>*optical double; naked-eye* | 3.57 | 4.24 | G9III | G3Ib | 340″ | 291° |
| $\delta^2$, $\delta^1$ Cha<br>*optical double; good colour contrast* | 4.5 | 5.5 | B3V | K0III | 265″ | 343° |
| α Cru | 1.1* | 4.9 | B1+B3 | B5 | 90″ | 202 |
| $o^1$, 30 Cyg<br>*optical double; good colour contrast* | 3.8 | 4.8 | K2II | A3III | 240″ | 324° |
| β Cyg<br>*Albireo* | 3.1 | 5.1 | K0 | A0 | 34″ | 054° |
| ν Dra | 4.9 | 4.9 | A5 | A5 | 60″ | 312° |
| $\delta^1$, $\delta^2$ Gru<br>*optical double; naked-eye* | 3.97 | 4.11 | G5 | M4 | 967″ | 161° |
| γ Lep | 3.7 | 6.3 | F8 | G5 | 96″ | 350° |
| $\alpha^1$, $\alpha^2$ Lib<br>*Zuben Elgenubi; optical double* | 2.8 | 5.2 | A2 | F5 | 231″ | 314° |
| ε Lyr<br>*famous as the 'double-double'* | 4.7* | 5.1* | A3+F1 | A5+F0 | 208″ | 173° |
| $\delta^2$, $\delta^1$ Lyr<br>*optical double; colour contrast* | 4.3 | 5.6 | M4 | B3.5 | 819″ | 349° |
| $\omega^1$, $\omega^2$ Sco<br>*optical double; naked-eye* | 3.96 | 4.32 | B1 | G2 | 877″ | 145° |
| $\nu^1$, $\nu^2$ Sgr<br>*optical double; naked-eye; lie on the ecliptic* | 4.83 | 4.99 | K2 | K3 | 821″ | 251° |
| $\theta^1$, $\theta^2$ Tau | 3.4 | 3.8 | F0 | K0 | 337″ | 366° |
| $\sigma^2$, $\sigma^1$ Tau | 4.7 | 5.1 | A3 | A2 | 431″ | 193° |
| κ, 67 Tau | 4.2 | 5.3 | A7 | A7 | 339″ | 173° |
| ζ, 80 UMa<br>*naked-eye double; Mizar, Alcor* | 2.3 | 4.0 | A0 | A5 | 710″ | 071° |
| γ Vel | 1.9 | 4.2 | 09 | B3 | 41″ | 220° |
| α, 8 Vul | 4.4 | 5.8 | M | K0 | 414″ | 028° |

**combined magnitude*

## Star clusters and galaxies

The tables list all star clusters and galaxies shown on the maps. The designation NGC refers to the listing in J.L.E.Dreyer's *New General Catalogue*, first published in 1888. Designation M refers to the listing in Charles Messier's catalogue of 1871.

Mag. represents integrated apparent magnitude for the whole object. Dia. represents the approximate diameter of an object in arcminutes (60 arcminutes = 1°).

| OPEN CLUSTERS | | | | | | |
|---|---|---|---|---|---|---|
| Designation | Name/Desig. | RA h min | Dec. deg min | Const. | Dia. | Mag. |
| NGC 457 | | 01 19.1 | +58 20 | Cas | 13′ | 6.4 |
| NGC 752 | | 01 57.8 | +37 41 | And | 50′ | 5.7 |
| NGC 869 | h Per | 02 19.0 | +57 09 | Per | 30′ | 4.3 |
| NGC 884 | c Per | 02 22.4 | +57 07 | Per | 30′ | 4.4 |
| NGC 869 & 884 make up the Double Cluster; naked-eye object | | | | | | |
| NGC 1039 | M34 | 02 42.0 | +42 47 | Per | 35′ | 5.2 |
| *naked-eye object under dark and clear conditions* | | | | | | |
| Pleiades | M45 | 03 47 | +24 07 | Tau | | 1.2 |
| *the Seven Sisters naked-eye cluster 390 ly away* | | | | | | |
| Hyades | | 04 25 | +16 | Tau | | 0.5 |
| *loose open cluster 140 ly away; Aldebaran moving across line of sight and not a member* | | | | | | |
| NGC 1912 | M38 | 05 28.7 | +35 50 | Aur | 21′ | 6.4 |
| NGC 1976 | M42 | 05 35.4 | –05 27 | Ori | 66′ | 4 |
| *Trapezium Cluster and Great Orion Nebula; naked-eye objects* | | | | | | |
| NGC 1960 | M36 | 05 36.1 | +34 08 | Aur | 12′ | 6.0 |
| NGC 2099 | M37 | 05 52.4 | +32 33 | Aur | 24′ | 5.6 |
| NGC 2168 | M35 | 06 08.9 | +24 20 | Gem | 28′ | 5.1 |
| NGC 2244 | | 06 32.4 | +04 52 | Mon | 24′ | 4.8 |
| *associated with the Rosette Nebula* | | | | | | |
| NGC 2264 | | 06 41.1 | +09 53 | Mon | 60′ | 3.9 |
| *associated with Cone Nebula (nebula visible only in photographs)* | | | | | | |
| NGC 2287 | M41 | 06 47.0 | –20 44 | CMa | 38′ | 4.5 |
| NGC 2362 | | 07 20.1 | –13 08 | CMa | 8′ | 4.1 |
| NGC 3422 | M47 | 07 36.6 | –14 30 | Pup | 30′ | 4.4 |
| *naked-eye object* | | | | | | |
| NGC 2437 | M46 | 07 41.8 | –14 49 | Pup | 2.7′ | 6.1 |
| *lies in same binocular field as M47* | | | | | | |
| NGC 2451 | | 07 45.4 | –37 58 | Pup | 45′ | 2.8 |
| NGC 2516 | | 07 58.3 | –60 52 | Car | 30′ | 3.8 |
| NGC 2548 | M48 | 08 13.8 | –05 48 | Hya | 54′ | 5.8 |
| NGC 2632 | M44 | 08 40.1 | +19 59 | Cnc | 95′ | 3.1 |
| *Praesepe or Beehive Cluster; naked-eye object* | | | | | | |
| IC 2391 | | 08 40.2 | –53 04 | Vel | 50′ | 2.5 |
| NGC 2682 | M67 | 08 50.4 | +11 49 | Cnc | 30′ | 6.9 |
| IC 2602 | q Car Cluster | 10 43.2 | –64 24 | Car | 50′ | 1.9 |
| *naked-eye object* | | | | | | |

| Designation | Name/Desig. | RA h min | Dec. deg min | Const. | Dia. | Mag. |
|---|---|---|---|---|---|---|
| NGC 3766 | | 11 36.1 | –61 37 | Cen | 12′ | 5.3 |
| Melotte 111 | | 12 25 | +26 | Com | 275′ | 1.8 |
| *naked eye cluster at 288 ly; includes stars in Ptolemy's 'Ivy Leaf'* | | | | | | |
| NGC 4755 | k Crucis Cluster | 12 53.6 | –60 20 | Cru | 10′ | 4.2 |
| *the Jewel Box Cluster; binocular object* | | | | | | |
| NGC 6067 | | 16 13.2 | –54 13 | Nor | 13′ | 5.6 |
| NGC 6087 | | 16 18.9 | –57 54 | Nor | 12′ | 5.4 |
| NGC 6231 | | 16 54 | –41 48 | Sco | 15′ | 2.6 |
| NGC 6405 | M6 | 17 40.1 | –32 13 | Sco | 15′ | 4.2 |
| IC 4665 | | 17 46.3 | +05 43 | Oph | 41′ | 4.2 |
| NGC 6475 | M7 | 17 53.9 | –34 49 | Sco | 80′ | 3.3 |
| NGC 6494 | M23 | 17 56.8 | –19 01 | Sgr | 27′ | 5.5 |
| NGC 6530 | M8 | 18 04.8 | –24 20 | Sgr | 15′ | 4.6 |
| *naked-eye cluster associated with the Lagoon Nebula* | | | | | | |
| NGC 6603 | M24 | 18 18.4 | –18 25 | Sgr | 5′ | 11 |
| *cluster in line of sight with what is predominantly a rich star field* | | | | | | |
| NGC 6705 | M11 | 18 51.1 | –06 16 | Sct | 14′ | 5.8 |
| *Wild Duck Cluster; binocular object* | | | | | | |
| NGC 6913 | M29 | 20 23.9 | +38 32 | Cyg | 7′ | 6.6 |
| NGC 7092 | M39 | 21 32.2 | +48 26 | Cyg | 32′ | 4.6 |
| NGC 7654 | M52 | 23 24.2 | +61 35 | Cas | 13′ | 6.9 |

## GLOBULAR CLUSTERS

| Designation | Name/Desig. | RA h min | Dec. deg min | Const. | Dia. | Mag. |
|---|---|---|---|---|---|---|
| NGC 104 | 47 Tuc | 00 24.1 | –72 05 | Tuc | 30.9 | 4.0 |
| *visible with naked eye* | | | | | | |
| NGC 5139 | ω Cen | 13 26.8 | –47 29 | Cen | 36.3 | 3.7 |
| *visible with naked eye* | | | | | | |
| NGC 5272 | M3 | 13 42.2 | +28 23 | CVn | 16.2 | 6.4 |
| NGC 5904 | M5 | 15 18.6 | +02 05 | SerCp | 17.4 | 5.8 |
| NGC 6121 | M4 | 16 23.6 | –26 32 | Sco | 26.3 | 5.9 |
| NGC 6205 | M13 | 16 41.7 | +36 28 | Her | 16.6 | 5.9 |
| NGC 6656 | M22 | 18 36.4 | –23 54 | Sgr | 24 | 5.1 |
| NGC 6752 | Dun 295 | 19 10.9 | –59 59 | Pav | 20.4 | 5.4 |

## EXTERNAL GALAXIES

| Designation | Name/Desig. | RA h min | Dec. deg min | Const. | Dia. | Mag. |
|---|---|---|---|---|---|---|
| NGC 224 | M31 | 00 24.7 | +41 16 | And | 178 | 3.5 |
| *Andromeda Galaxy; spiral galaxy at 2.15 Mly; naked-eye object* | | | | | | |
| Small Magellanic Cloud | | 01 | –72 | Tuc | | |
| *(SMC) dwarf irregular galaxy at 200,000 ly; associated with the Milky Way* | | | | | | |
| NGC 598 | M33 | 01 33.9 | +30 39 | Tri | 62 | 5.7 |
| *Triangulum Galaxy; spiral galaxy at 2.35 Mly; difficult naked-eye object* | | | | | | |
| Large Magellanic Cloud | | 05 30 | –69 | Dor/Men | | |
| *(LMC) dwarf irregular galaxy at 160,000ly; associated with the Milky Way* | | | | | | |

# The Solar System

There is a physical distinction between stars and planets. Stars are very large bodies of gas that create their own light from nuclear fusion processes in their interiors. The Sun is a star. Except for the Sun, all stars are very distant objects. The planets of the Solar System are (comparatively) small objects in orbit round the Sun, and the Earth is one of them. To the naked eye the planets Mercury, Venus, Mars, Jupiter and Saturn look like very bright stars, but their light is borrowed, reflected from the Sun.

The main difference that can be seen by the naked eye between stars and planets is that the stars hold fixed positions relative to each other but planets move: planets get their name from the Greek *astéres planetai*, meaning 'wandering stars'. The planets can be divided into two groups, inner and outer.

## *Inner and outer planets*

Mercury and Venus are called the 'inner planets' because their orbits are inside that of the Earth. Mars, Jupiter and Saturn are 'outer planets' because their orbits lie outside that of the Earth. These are the five planets known to the ancient world, although some early observers did not realize that the morning and evening apparitions of Venus and Mercury were of the same planets, so the phrase 'the seven stars' may derive from this confusion.

In 1781 a sixth planet was discovered and called Uranus; this was followed by Neptune in 1846 and by Pluto in 1930. Under suitable conditions an experienced observer can see Uranus with the naked eye;

▼ *The five naked-eye planets observed from the earliest times are the inner planets Mercury and Venus, and the outer planets Mars, Jupiter and Saturn. The red colour of Mars and the yellow colour of Saturn are clearly visible to the naked eye.*

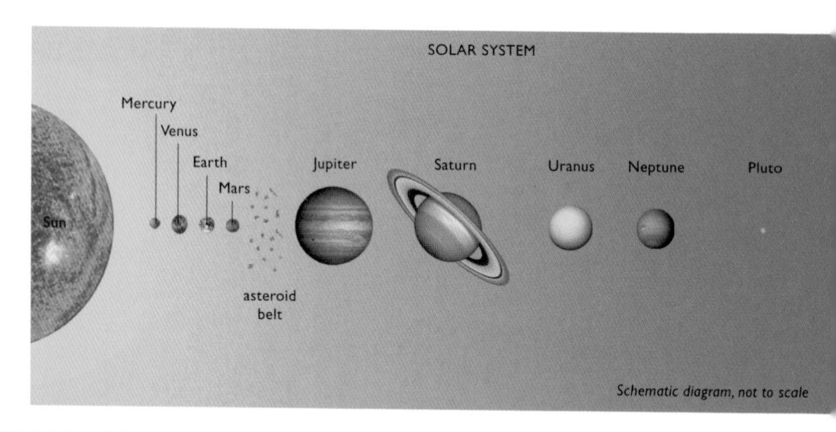

## THE SOLAR SYSTEM

| | |
|---|---|
| $m_v$ | Average brightness at elongation (☿, ♀) or at opposition (♂, ♃, ♄, ♅, ♆, ♇, ☽) |
| $D$ | Mean distance from Sun, in millions of kilometres |
| e | Eccentricity of elliptical orbit |
| $i_{orb}$ | Inclination of orbit relative to plane of ecliptic |
| $D_{pol}$ | Polar diameter in kilometres |
| $D_{equ}$ | Equatorial diameter in kilometres |
| $i_{equ}$ | Inclination of equator to plane of orbit |
| $M_{terr}$ | Mass expressed in Earth Masses |
| ρ | Density, expressed in grams per cubic centimetre |
| P | Sidereal period: time to complete one orbit relative to fixed stars |
| S | Synodic period: time to return to same position relative to Sun as observed from Earth |
| moons | Number of natural satellites |
| dl | Day length in terrestrial hours (1 terrestrial day = 24 hours) |

Measures given in italics are relative to Earth; measures marked with an asterisk* are given for a surface defined at atmospheric pressure one bar.

| | $m_v$ | D | e | $i_{orb}$ | $i_{equ}$ | $D_{pol}$ | $D_{equ}$ |
|---|---|---|---|---|---|---|---|
| ☿ Mercury | –0.2 | 57.9 | 0.206 | 7.0° | 0.0° | 4,879 | 4,879 |
| ♀ Venus | –4.2 | 108.2 | 0.007 | 3.4° | 177.3° | — | 12,104 |
| ⊕ Earth | — | 149.6 | 0.017 | — | 23.45° | 2,714 | 12,756 |
| ♂ Mars | –2.0 | 227.9 | 0.094 | 1.9° | 25.19° | 6,750 | 6,794 |
| ♃ Jupiter | –2.5 | 778 | 0.049 | 1.3° | 3.13° | 133,710* | 142,980* |
| ♄ Saturn | 0.7 | 1427 | 0.057 | 2.5° | 26.73° | 108,730* | 120,540* |
| ♅ Uranus | 5.5 | 2870 | 0.046 | 0.8° | 97.77° | 49,950* | 51,120* |
| ♆ Neptune | 7.9 | 4497 | 0.011 | 1.8° | 28.32° | 48,680* | 49,530* |
| ♇ Pluto | 14.9 | 5900 | 0.249 | 17.2° | 122.53° | 2,250 | 2,250 |
| ☽ Moon | –12.74 | — | *0.55* | *5.145°* | 6.68° | 3,472 | 3,476 |

| | $M_{terr}$ | ρ | P | S | moons | dl |
|---|---|---|---|---|---|---|
| Mercury | *0.056* | 5.6 | 87.97d | 115.88d | 0 | 4223 |
| Venus | *0.8148* | 5.1 | 224.70d | 583.92 | 0 | 2802 |
| Earth | *1* | 5.52 | 365.256d | — | 1 | 24 |
| Mars | *0.107* | 3.93 | 686.98d | 779.94d | 2 | 24.7 |
| Jupiter | *317.82* | 1.30 | 11.87y | 398.88d | 63 | 9.9 |
| Saturn | *95.2* | 0.69 | 29.46y | 378.09d | 33 | 10.7 |
| Uranus | *14.5* | 1.3 | 84.01y | 369.66d | 27 | 17.2 |
| Neptune | *17.1* | 1.6 | 164.79y | 367.49 | 13 | 16.1 |
| Pluto | *0.002* | 1.8 | 247.7y | 366.73d | 1 | 153.3 |
| Moon | *0.0123* | 3.35 | *27.32d* | *29.53d* | — | 708.7 |

Sun $m_v$: –26.74
mean diameter: 1,399,000 km
rotation period at latitude 16°: 609.12h
$M_{terr}$: 1,989,100
ρ: 1.4 gr/cc
luminosity: 384.6 × $10^{24}$ J/s

it looks like a very faint star. Uranus is more easily observed with the help of binoculars, detailed tables, and a star map more detailed than the ones in this book. Neptune and Pluto are telescope objects.

The Earth and all the other planets except Pluto orbit the Sun in much the same plane, and seen from Earth they keep close to the ecliptic. The outer planets, Mars, Jupiter and Saturn, move in apparent independence of the Sun in an overall easterly direction. The inner planets, Mercury and Venus, appear tied to the Sun, and are seen only in the western sky after sunset or in the eastern sky before dawn.

Mercury is only seen as an object close to the horizon in twilight. Venus is brilliant white, seen further from the horizon than Mercury, and for periods in darkness. Mars is observed in darkness, sometimes brilliant, always red. Jupiter appears brilliant white, sometimes with an orange tint. Saturn is dimmer and appears yellow.

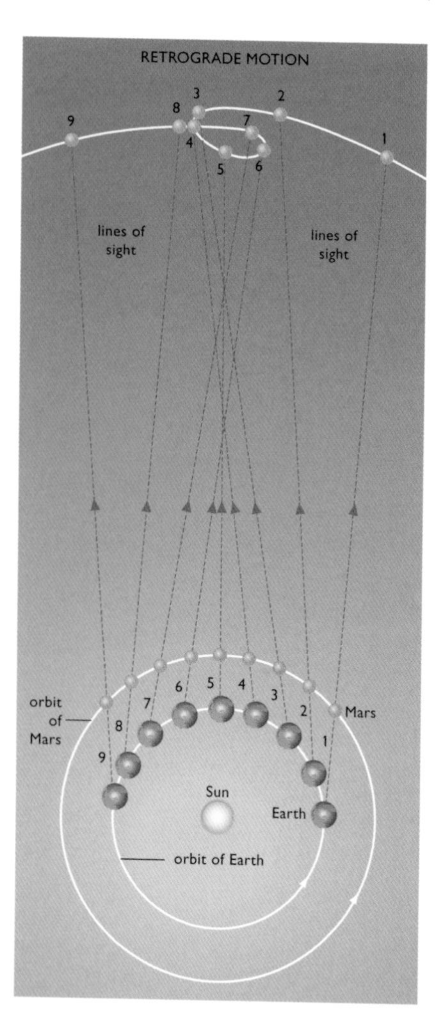


◀ *The diagram shows the Earth overtaking Mars on the inside. The looping path at the head of the diagram shows the apparent movement of Mars seen from Earth. From positions 3 to 7 Mars appears to slow down (3), stop (4), move backwards (5), stop (6) and move forwards again (7). The seeming backward movement at 5 is called retrograde motion.*

### Direct and retrograde motion

Observed from the Earth the planets show an overall motion from west to east along the path of the ecliptic. This easterly movement is called direct motion, and it reflects the true direction of the planets' orbits round the Sun. However, the closer a planet is to the Sun the faster it orbits, and as the Earth passes between the Sun

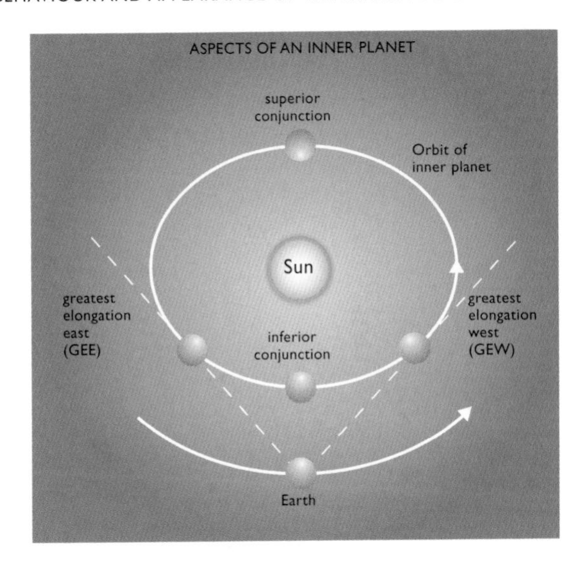


▶ *Apparitions of the inner planets. Mercury and Venus have orbits inside that of the Earth. At greatest elongation east they appear as evening objects. They disappear as they move between the Earth and the Sun, and reappear as morning objects towards greatest elongation west.*

and an outer planet, overtaking it on the inside, the planet goes through a period when it appears to move backwards against the fixed stars – east to west – in apparent, 'retrograde' motion. Retrograde motion is also seen when an inner planet passes between the Earth and the Sun, but because the inner planets are mostly observed in twilight, retrogression against the fixed stars is not very obvious.

### *Behaviour and appearance of the inner planets*

At superior conjunction an inner planet lies on the far side of the Sun from Earth and cannot be seen. As it moves into elongation east (elongation means angular separation from the Sun) it becomes visible as an evening object, one that sets in the west after the Sun. After greatest elongation east (GEE) it moves back towards the Sun. At inferior conjunction it passes between the Earth and the Sun and cannot be seen. As it moves into elongation west it reappears as a morning object, rising in the east before the Sun. After greatest elongation west (GEW) it turns back towards the Sun and disappears on its way towards superior conjunction.

### *Apparitions of Mercury*

The greatest elongation of Mercury ranges from 18° to 280°, making some apparitions more difficult than others. Searches should be made for about 30 minutes, starting 40 minutes after sunset (evening apparition, easiest in spring) or 70 minutes before sunrise (morning apparition, easiest in autumn). The first search should be made a few days

▲ *Mercury is fleetingly visible in the area of sky close to the twilit horizon, illuminated by the nearby but hidden Sun.*

before greatest elongation. The sky needs to be clear almost to the level of the horizon. Mercury appears as a starlike object 6–18° above the horizon in the region blanched by the hidden Sun.

Mercury at elongation varies in brightness from $m_V$ +1 to −1, on average rather brighter than any star that might appear nearby. In an evening observation Mercury is likely to be the first starlike object to become visible close to the western horizon, and in a morning observation the last starlike object to rise in the lightening eastern sky. From one evening apparition of Mercury to the next takes four months (synodic period 115.88 days). From GEE to GEW takes 45 days, while GEW to GEE takes 75 days.

| GREATEST ELONGATIONS OF MERCURY EAST (EVENING APPARITION) | | | | | |
|---|---|---|---|---|---|
| 2005 | Nov 03 | 2012 | Jul 01 | 2019 | Feb 27 |
| 2006 | Feb 24 | 2012 | Oct 26 | 2019 | Jun 23 |
| 2006 | Jun 20 | 2013 | Feb 16 | 2019 | Oct 20 |
| 2006 | Oct 17 | 2013 | Jun 12 | 2020 | Feb 10 |
| 2007 | Feb 07 | 2013 | Oct 09 | 2020 | Jun 04 |
| 2007 | Jun 02 | 2014 | Jan 31 | 2020 | Oct 01 |
| 2007 | Sep 29 | 2014 | May 25 | 2021 | Jan 24 |
| 2008 | Jan 22 | 2014 | Sep 21 | 2021 | May 17 |
| 2008 | May 14 | 2015 | Jan 14 | 2021 | Sep 14 |
| 2008 | Sep 11 | 2015 | May 07 | 2022 | Jan 07 |
| 2009 | Jan 04 | 2015 | Sep 04 | 2022 | Apr 29 |
| 2009 | Apr 26 | 2015 | Dec 29 | 2022 | Aug 27 |
| 2009 | Aug 24 | 2016 | Apr 18 | 2022 | Dec 21 |
| 2009 | Dec 18 | 2016 | Aug 16 | 2023 | Apr 11 |
| 2010 | Apr 08 | 2016 | Dec 11 | 2023 | Aug 10 |
| 2010 | Aug 07 | 2017 | Apr 01 | 2023 | Dec 04 |
| 2010 | Dec 01 | 2017 | Jul 30 | 2024 | Mar 24 |
| 2011 | Mar 23 | 2017 | Nov 24 | 2024 | Jul 22 |
| 2011 | Jul 20 | 2018 | Mar 15 | 2024 | Nov 16 |
| 2011 | Nov 14 | 2018 | Jul 12 | 2025 | Mar 08 |
| 2012 | Mar 05 | 2018 | Nov 06 | 2025 | Jul 04 |
| | | | | 2025 | Oct 29 |

| GREATEST ELONGATIONS OF MERCURY WEST (MORNING APPARITION) | | | | | |
|---|---|---|---|---|---|
| 2005 | Dec 12 | 2012 | Aug 16 | 2019 | Apr 11 |
| 2006 | Apr 08 | 2012 | Dec 04 | 2019 | Aug 09 |
| 2006 | Aug 07 | 2013 | Mar 31 | 2019 | Nov 28 |
| 2006 | Nov 25 | 2013 | Jul 30 | 2020 | Mar 24 |
| 2007 | Mar 22 | 2013 | Nov 18 | 2020 | Jul 22 |
| 2007 | Jul 20 | 2014 | Mar 14 | 2020 | Nov 10 |
| 2007 | Nov 08 | 2014 | Jul 12 | 2021 | Mar 06 |
| 2008 | Mar 03 | 2014 | Nov 01 | 2021 | Jul 04 |
| 2008 | Jul 01 | 2015 | Feb 24 | 2021 | Oct 25 |
| 2008 | Oct 22 | 2015 | Jun 24 | 2022 | Feb 16 |
| 2009 | Feb 13 | 2015 | Oct 16 | 2022 | Jun 16 |
| 2009 | Jun 13 | 2016 | Feb 07 | 2022 | Oct 08 |
| 2009 | Oct 06 | 2016 | Jun 05 | 2023 | Jan 30 |
| 2010 | Jan 27 | 2016 | Sep 28 | 2023 | May 29 |
| 2010 | May 26 | 2017 | Jan 19 | 2023 | Sep 22 |
| 2010 | Sep 19 | 2017 | May 17 | 2024 | Jan 12 |
| 2011 | Jan 09 | 2017 | Sep 12 | 2024 | May 09 |
| 2011 | May 07 | 2018 | Jan 01 | 2024 | Sep 05 |
| 2011 | Sep 03 | 2018 | Apr 29 | 2024 | Dec 25 |
| 2011 | Dec 23 | 2018 | Aug 26 | 2025 | Apr 21 |
| 2012 | Apr 18 | 2018 | Dec 15 | 2025 | Aug 19 |
| | | | | 2025 | Dec 07 |

## *Apparitions of Venus*

From one evening apparition of Venus to the next takes 19 months (synodic period 583.92 days). GEE to GEW takes 20 weeks, and GEW to GEE takes 63 weeks.

Venus becomes visible as an evening object four months before GEE and becomes easy to find two months before. At GEE it reaches 45–47° of separation from the Sun, and brightens. To the naked eye it looks like a brilliant white starlike object, but through binoculars the planet is seen in a crescent phase.

After GEE the planet turns back towards the Sun, but continues to brighten for five weeks, reaching a maximum of $m_V$ −4.4 (15 times brighter than Sirius) before accelerating in apparent motion towards

| GREATEST ELONGATIONS OF VENUS EAST (evening apparition) AND WEST (morning apparition) | | | | | | | | |
|---|---|---|---|---|---|---|---|---|
| GEE | | GEW | GEE | | GEW | GEE | | GEW |
| Nov 03 | 2005 | — | Mar 27 | 2012 | Aug 15 | — | 2019 | Jan 06 |
| — | 2006 | Mar 25 | Nov 01 | 2013 | — | Mar 24 | 2020 | — |
| Jun 09 | 2007 | Oct 28 | — | 2014 | Mar 22 | Oct 29 | 2021 | — |
| — | 2008 | — | Jun 06 | 2015 | Oct 26 | — | 2022 | Mar 20 |
| Jan 14 | 2009 | Jun 05 | — | 2016 | — | Jan 04 | 2023 | Oct 23 |
| Aug 20 | 2010 | — | Jan 12 | 2017 | Jun 03 | — | 2024 | — |
| — | 2011 | Jan 08 | Aug 17 | 2018 | — | Jan 10 | 2025 | Jun 01 |

◀ *Venus as an evening star is likely to be the most brilliant object in the western sky after sunset. Here the planet is seen in company with a crescent Moon, a conjunction that can be enjoyed at some time in every apparition of the planet.*

the Sun, and fading abruptly from sight.

Three weeks after inferior conjunction the planet appears in the morning sky and with equal abruptness flares up in two weeks to $m_V$ −4.4, reached five weeks before GEW. After GEW the planet slowly turns back towards the Sun, fades, and disappears after about four months.

## *Behaviour and appearance of the outer planets*

At conjunction the outer planets, Mars, Jupiter and Saturn, are hidden by the Sun. They are first visible a month (two months for Mars) after conjunction as morning objects that rise in the east before dawn. On each morning that follows the planet rises earlier. At quadrature west the planet rises at midnight and reaches the meridian at dawn. At opposition it rises at sunset, passes the meridian at midnight, and sets at dawn.

When the planet reaches quadrature east it comes out on the meridian at sunset, and sets at midnight. After quadrature east the planet appears progressively lower in the western sky after sunset, until a month or so before conjunction, when it becomes lost in the afterglow of the setting Sun.

Mars, Jupiter and Saturn are at their brightest at opposition, when the Earth is nearest to them. They are at their most conveniently placed for evening observation from this time

ASPECTS OF AN OUTER PLANET

from this position outer planet is seen at quadrature west

from this position outer planet first seen rising before sunrise

outer planet

Sun

orbit of Earth

planet observed at opposition

orbit of outer planet

from this position outer planet is seen at quadrature east

from this position outer planet last seen setting after sunset

◀ *Outer planets become visible as morning objects, brighten through quadrature, and reach maximum brilliance at opposition to Sun.*

through to quadrature east. Over this period they are seen rising in the east in the evening.

For most of each apparition the planet shows an eastward (direct) motion against the stars but around opposition it retrogrades (see page 56). The retrograde motion begins at a point somewhere between quadrature west and opposition, and returns to direct motion at a point between opposition and quadrature east.

Jupiter and Mars at opposition are easily distinguished from stars: Jupiter at opposition ($m_V$ −2.3 to −2.9) is brighter than any star, and Mars ($m_V$ −1.0 to −2.8) is far brighter than any star in whose company it might appear. Jupiter is cream-orange, Mars is conspicuously red. Saturn appears no brighter than a very bright star ($m_V \approx 0.7$) but it has a distinctly yellow colour. Saturn moves so little from one year to the next that the observer has only to identify the planet once in order to find it again the next year.

## *Oppositions of Mars*

Mars returns to opposition in about 780 days (2 years and 7 weeks). The planet's orbit is markedly eccentric, so that oppositions range from 40° to 70° east of the one that came before. The planet completes a full circuit of the ecliptic between oppositions (so the distance it travels is in fact 400° to 430°). Retrograde motion starts 5 weeks before opposition, lasts 10 weeks, and covers 15°.

▲ *Mars and Jupiter in Taurus. Mars is seen upper centre, Aldebaran middle left, Jupiter lower right centre, the Pleiades right centre. To the naked eye the outer planets appear like bright or very bright stars.*

| OPPOSITIONS OF MARS | | | | | | | | |
|---|---|---|---|---|---|---|---|---|
| date | | ecliptic | date | | ecliptic | date | | ecliptic |
| 2005 | Nov 07 | 045° | 2012 | Mar 04 | 154° | 2019 | – | |
| 2006 | – | | 2013 | – | | 2020 | Oct 13 | 021° |
| 2007 | Dec 24 | 093° | 2014 | Apr 08 | 189° | 2021 | – | |
| 2008 | – | | 2015 | – | | 2022 | Dec 09 | 076° |
| 2009 | – | | 2016 | May 22 | 242° | 2023 | – | |
| 2010 | Jan 29 | 140° | 2017 | – | | 2024 | – | |
| 2011 | – | | 2018 | Jul 27 | 304° | 2025 | Jan 16 | 116° |

◀ *The four brightest moons of Jupiter are visible in this view through a small telescope. The moons are visible as pricks of light close by the planet when observed in a pair of good binoculars, although the characteristic banding of the planet will not be visible.*

## Oppositions of Jupiter

Jupiter returns to opposition just over one month later each year, with each opposition 30° or more east of the one that preceded it. Retrograde motion starts eight weeks before opposition, lasts 16 weeks, and covers 10°.

| OPPOSITIONS OF JUPITER | | | | | | | | |
|---|---|---|---|---|---|---|---|---|
| date | | ecliptic | date | | ecliptic | date | | ecliptic |
| 2006 | May 04 | 224° | 2013 | – | | 2020 | Jul 14 | 292° |
| 2007 | Jun 05 | 255° | 2014 | Jan 05 | 105° | 2021 | Aug 20 | 327° |
| 2008 | Jul 09 | 287° | 2015 | Feb 06 | 138° | 2022 | Sep 26 | 004° |
| 2009 | Aug 14 | 322° | 2016 | Mar 08 | 168° | 2023 | Nov 03 | 040° |
| 2010 | Sep 21 | 358° | 2017 | Apr 07 | 198° | 2024 | Dec 07 | 076° |
| 2011 | Oct 29 | 035° | 2018 | May 09 | 228° | 2026 | Jan 10 | 110° |
| 2012 | Dec 03 | 071° | 2019 | Jun 10 | 259° | 2027 | Feb 11 | 142° |

## Oppositions of Saturn

Saturn returns to opposition two weeks later each year, with each opposition found approximately 13° east of the one that came before. Retrograde motion starts 10 weeks before opposition, lasts 20 weeks, and covers 7°.

◀ *The characteristic yellow cast of Saturn can seen in a break in the clouds to the left of the Moon. Rain-washed skies and racing cloud create areas of great clarity, exciting conditions for star and planet spotting.*

| OPPOSITIONS OF SATURN | | | | | | | | |
|---|---|---|---|---|---|---|---|---|
| date | | ecliptic | date | | ecliptic | date | | ecliptic |
| 2006 | Jan 27 | 128° | 2013 | Apr 28 | 218° | 2020 | Jul 20 | 299° |
| 2007 | Feb 10 | 142° | 2014 | May 10 | 230° | 2021 | Aug 02 | 310° |
| 2008 | Feb 24 | 155° | 2015 | May 23 | 242° | 2022 | Aug 14 | 322° |
| 2009 | Mar 08 | 168° | 2016 | Jun 03 | 253° | 2023 | Aug 27 | 334° |
| 2010 | Mar 22 | 181° | 2017 | Jun 15 | 264° | 2024 | Sep 08 | 246° |
| 2011 | Apr 03 | 194° | 2018 | Jun 27 | 276° | 2025 | Sep 21 | 359° |
| 2012 | Apr 15 | 206° | 2019 | Jul 09 | 287° | 2026 | Oct 12 | 011° |

## *Meteor Showers*

Meteors are seen as sudden streaks of light across the sky. They are produced when a piece of interplanetary material is vaporized in the Earth's atmosphere. On rare occasions the fragment is sufficiently large to survive its fall and may be recovered as a meteorite. The Earth's orbit passes through patches of interplanetary dust that produce predictable showers. Each shower appears to radiate from a particular point in the sky and is named after the constellation in which the radiant is found.

Meteors are not to be confused with comets, most of which appear as indistinct objects that take weeks to cross the sky. Points of light seen in steady motion close to the zenith are produced by sunlight reflected from artificial satellites.

▲ *Two Leonid meteors are captured moving southwest in this photograph of a skyfield in Orion. Tracing their path backwards produces a crossover in Leo, the radiant.*

| METEOR SHOWERS | | | |
|---|---|---|---|
| January 3 | Quadrantids* | October 20 | Orionids |
| (radiant RA 15h 30m Dec.50°N) | | November 5 | Taurids |
| April 21 | Lyrids | November 16 | Leonids |
| May 4 | Eta Aquarids | December 13 | Geminids |
| August 4 | Delta Aquarids | December 22 | Ursids |
| August 11 | Perseids | (radiant RA 14h 30m Dec.80°N) | |
| *Quadrans was a minor constellation, now abandoned | | | |

# More titles from the Philip's Astronomy range

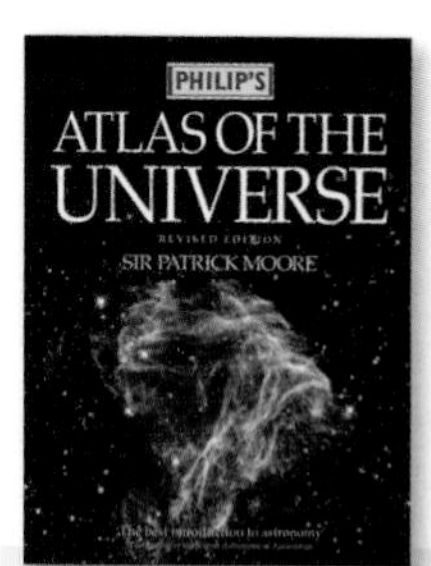


### *Philip's Atlas of the Universe*

Sir Patrick Moore
ISBN 0 540 08791 2 £25.00

- Our Solar System and its place in the Universe
- Includes a complete atlas of the constellations and a Moon map

***'... claims to deliver the cosmos and succeeds spectacularly'*** *Times Literary Supplement*

### *Philip's Night Sky Atlas*

Robin Scagell
ISBN 0 540 08700 9 £14.99

- Comprehensive star atlas, robustly produced for practical use in the field
- Photo-realistic images to help match the mapping with the sky

### *Philip's Practical Astronomy*

Storm Dunlop
ISBN 0 540 07958 8 £9.99

- Ideal introduction to observational astronomy
- Illustrated with more than 150 colour images

***'... attractive, clearly written and includes all a beginner would need to know to get started'*** *Popular Astronomy*

### *Philip's Stargazing with a Telescope*

Robin Scagell
ISBN 0 540 08478 6 £9.99

- An essential guide to choosing and using a telescope
- Includes lists of objects to observe and star maps

## *Philip's Planispheres*

Rotate the disc to reveal the stars visible from your location at any time on any night of the year. The 51.5°N and 35°S editions come with a season-by-season guide to exploring the skies.

Planisphere 51.5°N
• UK, Northern Europe, Canada
• ISBN 0 540 08817 X • £7.99

Also available 42°N (Southern Europe, USA, Japan), 32°N (Middle East, Northern Africa), 23.5°N (Mexico, Caribbean, India) and 35°S (Australia, New Zealand, South America, Southern Africa).

### *Also available...*

***Solar System Observer's Guide***
Peter Grego • ISBN 0 540 08827 7 • £9.99

***Deep Sky Observer's Guide***
Neil Bone • ISBN 0 540 08585 5 • £9.99

***Moon Observer's Guide***
Peter Grego • ISBN 0 540 08419 0 • £9.99

***Sun Observer's Guide***
Pam Spence • ISBN 0 540 08393 3 • £9.99

***Mars Observer's Guide***
Neil Bone • ISBN 0 540 08387 9 • £8.99

***Star Chart***
ISBN 0 540 08416 6 • £5.99

***Moon Map***
ISBN 0 540 06378 9 • £6.99

***Deep Sky Chart***
ISBN 0 540 08733 5 • £6.99

## ☏ How to order

The Philip's range of Astronomy Titles is available from bookshops or directly from the publisher by phoning 01903 828503 or online at www.philips-maps.co.uk

*Prices are correct at time of going to press but are subject to change without notification*